Isla McIntosh

Guide
to
Standard Grade
Biology

by

Robert McMath, B.Sc.

ISBN 0 7169 3177 x
© *R. McMath, 1993*
(Revised 1996)

ROBERT GIBSON · Publisher
17 Fitzroy Place, Glasgow, G3 7SF.

INTRODUCTION

This book has been written with one aim in mind: to help you pass Standard Grade Biology.

The book is not intended as a text book to be used in the classroom or laboratory, but as a revision aid to help you prepare for tests and examinations.

Its aim is simply to set out in a clear and concise form what you have to **know** and **understand** in order to do well in Standard Grade Biology.

Don't forget that in your examination you will also be expected to show certain **problem solving** skills, such as drawing or interpreting diagrams and graphs and drawing comparisons and conclusions. These skills will also be helped by a good knowledge and understanding of Standard Grade Biology, which can be gained by studying this book.

Be prepared — and good luck!

ADVICE TO USERS

How to Use This Book

Standard Grade Biology consists of 7 topics.

1. The Biosphere
2. Investigating Cells
3. The World of Plants
4. Animal Survival
5. The Body in Action
6. Inheritance
7. Biotechnology.

Each of these topics is divided up into a number of sub-topics. You will find that this book follows this pattern with a separate chapter for each sub-topic.

In each chapter, what is relevant to General Level work is set out first and what is relevant to Credit Level comes at the end of the chapter.

Each separate piece of General or Credit work is identified by a number in a box, e.g.

G1 or C3 etc.

Beside each box you will find a short piece of writing in *italics*. This is a very brief description of *what you should be able to do* after completing this piece of work. These can be used as checkpoints for your final revision. Go through the book and at each checkpoint ask yourself, "Can I do that?" If not, work through the section again.

If you wish to study the Credit material, (and you are recommended to do so), you must first cover the General Level work and whenever you come across a sign like this

$\Rightarrow$ C1/9

you should turn to the appropriate Credit Level material (labelled, e.g. C1) at the end of the chapter. The number following the C1 is, in this instance, the relevant page number which you should refer to (i.e. page 9).

CONTENTS

SUB-TOPIC (a) — Investigating an Ecosystem

GENERAL LEVEL

G1 *[Identify the parts of which an ecosystem is composed, i.e. the habitats and the plants and animals living there.]*

As well as studying the plants and animals (including humans), an investigation of an ecosystem must also include a study of the 'place' itself. An investigation of a woodland ecosystem would have to include a study of the position of the wood. Is it sheltered or exposed? Is it on flat ground or on a slope? Perhaps even a study of the underlying rock would be needed as this influences the soil.

The place where an organism lives is called its **habitat**. Within each ecosystem there may be a number of different habitats, each with its own wide variety of plants and animals.

Sampling organisms

G2 *[Give an example of a sampling technique used to estimate the population and distribution of organisms in a habitat and describe its use.]*

Sampling techniques are used to find out what (and approximately how many) animals and plants are present in an ecosystem as it is usually impossible to count all members of a population.

Netting

Sweep nets with very fine mesh are swept through the branches of bushes and trees to catch small flying insects. These may be transferred to specimen jars for later identification.

Pond nets have coarser mesh to allow water to pass through easily whilst trapping small water organisms such as water beetles and water dwelling insect larvae. In a stream, the net is held downstream and organisms, dislodged by kicking the bed of the stream, are carried into the net.

Quadrats

A *quadrat* is a square frame of a known area (usually 1 m²). It is thrown at **random** in the area to be studied. The number of plants or animals of the type being investigated that are within the quadrat, are counted. This is repeated a number of times. The more times it is repeated, the more accurate the population estimate will be.

The population of daisies in a lawn could be estimated as follows:

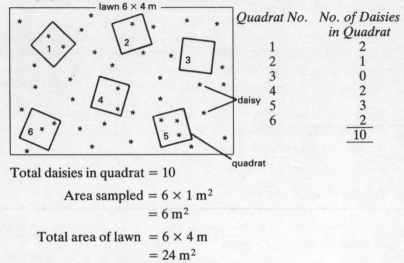

Quadrat No.	No. of Daisies in Quadrat
1	2
2	1
3	0
4	2
5	3
6	2
	10

Total daisies in quadrat = 10

$$\text{Area sampled} = 6 \times 1 \text{ m}^2$$
$$= 6 \text{ m}^2$$

$$\text{Total area of lawn} = 6 \times 4 \text{ m}$$
$$= 24 \text{ m}^2$$

10 daisies were found in 6 m², therefore in 24 m² (four times as much) we would expect to find 4 × 10 = 40 daisies.

Count the daisies in the "lawn" above to see how close the estimate comes to the true number.

Trapping

A *pitfall trap* can be used to catch crawling invertebrates from the leaf litter layer of a woodland floor or a field.

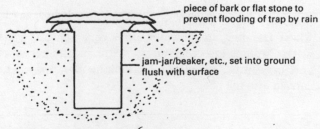

6

Small mammals can be live-trapped in baited traps made of metal or plastic.

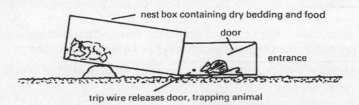

Animals may be marked and released, unharmed, from these traps.

$\Rightarrow$ C1/9

Abiotic factors

G3 *[Name two abiotic factors.]*

G4 *[Give an example of a technique which might be used to measure an abiotic factor and describe its use.]*

The distribution of plants and animals is affected not only by the other plants and animals (the biotic factors) present in their habitat, but also by non-living (abiotic) factors.

Habitat	Abiotic Factor	Measurement Technique
Woodland	soil temperature	soil thermometer / electronic thermometer
	air temperature	mercury thermometer
	soil moisture	soil moisture probe / weigh-dry-weigh soil sample
	soil pH	pH probe and meter / pH indicator paper or universal indicator solution
	light intensity	light meter
Fresh water stream	water temperature	mercury / electronic thermometer
	light intensity under water	light meter with separate light probe
	oxygen content of water	oxygen electrode and meter / chemical analysis
	flow rate	float timed over measured distance

Errors must be avoided in the measurement of abiotic factors.

$\Rightarrow$ C2/11

The distribution of Living Organisms

[G5] *[State the effect an abiotic factor has on the distribution of organisms.]*

The distribution of plants and animals is brought about by many different factors. Climatic factors ("weather") have a major influence on plant and animal distribution. These non-living, or **abiotic** factors, include:

> temperature
> rainfall (or soil moisture)
> amount of light
> wind.

Although Scotland is a small country, different parts of Scotland will experience each of these abiotic factors to a different extent. For example, the south-east tends to be warmer and sunnier than the north-west. The west coast has higher rainfall than the east coast. The Outer Hebrides are more exposed to wind than the mainland.

On an even more local scale, each of these abiotic factors will vary over distances of only a few metres. A woodland floor will be cooler and darker than a corn field only 20 metres away. A hilltop will be windier than a valley, but the valley soil will probably be deeper and damper than the hilltop soil.

All of these factors will determine what plants are able to grow in a particular place and the plants, in turn, will help to determine what animals can live there.

$\Rightarrow$ C3/12

CREDIT LEVEL

Sampling errors

C1 *[Identify a possible source of error that might be involved in a sampling technique and explain how it might be reduced.]*

Errors in sampling, giving an estimate of a population which may be either too high or too low, can arise for a number of reasons.

1. *Not enough samples taken.* Go back to the diagram on page 6 and work out the estimated population if only quadrats 1 and 3 had been counted. You should find that this gives an answer that is far too low.

2. *Samples too closely grouped.* This would not take account of the obvious clumping of daisies on this lawn.

3. *Deliberate placing of sample sites.* Deliberately choosing "good" sites would give too high an estimate of daisies on this lawn.

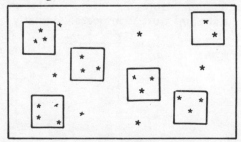

The same errors apply to any sampling technique, e.g. pitfall traps, small mammal traps, etc.

How to reduce errors in sampling

Errors can be reduced by:

1. Taking adequate number of samples.

2. Avoiding the tendency to take samples from "good looking" sites. This can be done by choosing sample sites at **random**, or by taking samples on a **grid pattern**, e.g.

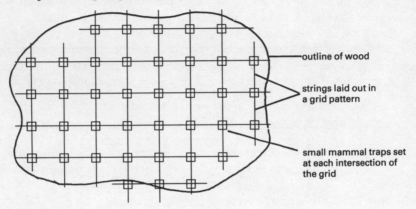

outline of wood

strings laid out in a grid pattern

small mammal traps set at each intersection of the grid

Errors which may arise due to incorrect use of the sampling equipment must also be avoided. Care must be taken when using quadrats to count only those individual plants and animals which are at least half inside the quadrat. Care must also be taken to ensure that organisms sampled are correctly identified.

Pitfall traps, mammal traps, etc., must be set so that animals are able to enter the traps and must be inspected regularly.

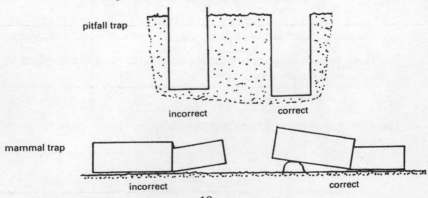

pitfall trap

incorrect   correct

mammal trap

incorrect   correct

Recording errors

C2 *[Identify a possible source of error that might occur during the measurement of an abiotic factor and explain how it might be reduced.]*

Common errors of this type are:

1. failing to give thermometers long enough for the mercury to stop rising/falling

2. failing to allow meter needles to stop moving before taking a reading

3. casting a shadow over a light meter.

Errors in making comparisons of a number of sites

1. Weather conditions or time of day may have been different when sites were investigated.

2. Probes (e.g. soil thermometer, soil moisture, etc.) may not have been pushed into the soil to the same depth at different sites.

How to reduce errors in recording abiotic factors

Avoiding these errors is done simply by correctly carrying out the techniques used, e.g.

1. Give thermometers long enough to stabilise before taking a reading.

2. Allow meters (pH, moisture, light, etc.) to stabilise before taking a reading. (Make sure you use the correct scale.)

3. Avoid casting a shadow over a light meter.

4. When making a comparison of different sites, make sure readings are taken under similar conditions, e.g. time of day, similar weather, etc.

5. Make sure probes (temperature, moisture, etc.) are handled in the same way at each site.

6. Take a number of readings at each site and work out an average.

The effect of abiotic factors on distribution of organisms

C3 *[Explain ways in which abiotic factors can influence the distribution of organisms.]*

Without detailed study of an organism and its habitat, we can only suggest possible ways in which abiotic factors might affect its distribution. This is because a number of factors will be involved, not just a single one.

Example 1

The simple green plant *Pleurococcus* grows on the wettest side of a tree trunk. But wind direction (blowing against the tree) and light intensity (without which the plant cannot photosynthesise) will also influence its growth.

Example 2

The common dogwhelk, found on rocky shores, is only found where winter sea temperatures are between −1 °C and 19 °C. On each shore where they are found, however, their local distribution will be affected by wave action and availability of food (a biotic factor).

SUB-TOPIC (b) — How it Works

GENERAL LEVEL

G1 *[Describe what is meant by the words habitat, population, community and ecosystem.]*

The word **habitat** was introduced earlier in the first chapter. It means the place where a plant or animal lives. Some other important terms used in this chapter are:

Population   All the members of the same species living in a particular area form a population.

Community   All the populations of plants and animals in a particular area make up a community.

Ecosystem   The community plus the non-living environment in a particular area make up an ecosystem.

G2 *[Describe what is meant by the words producer and consumer.]*

A community of plants and animals needs a lot of food to keep it alive. The plant populations in a community can use the energy of sunlight to make their own food. Because they do this, plants are called **producers**. Animals cannot make their own food and so must eat plants or other animals. They are therefore called **consumers**.

Summary   Green plants are **producers**.
               Animals (and non-green plants like fungi) are **consumers**.

Note: **Herbivore** = a consumer which eats only plants
       Carnivore = a consumer which eats only animals
       Omnivore = a consumer which eats both plants and animals.

G3 *[Give an example of a food chain and a food web.]*

G4 *[State that the arrows in a food web diagram show the direction of the flow of energy.]*

Food Chains

A food chain is a simple way to describe how members of a community depend upon one another for food. For example, on the grasslands of the

African savannah, zebras and lions, along with the grass, form a simple community.

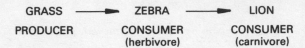

GRASS ⟶ ZEBRA ⟶ LION

PRODUCER   CONSUMER   CONSUMER
              (herbivore)   (carnivore)

The arrows in a food chain always point **from** the organism that is being eaten, **to** the eater. This is because the arrows show the direction of the **flow of energy** through the chain.

Although it is not usually shown in a food chain, the sun provides the energy for the plant.

A food chain must always start with a green plant.

Food Webs

Food chains are very simple and do not show how complex the feeding relationships in a community really are. For example, in the food chain above, zebras do not only eat grass; there will be other green plants in their diet. Lions do not only eat zebras; they will also eat gazelle, wildebeest, etc.

A more complete picture of the feeding relationships in a community is given by a **food web**.

Part of a typical African savannah food web

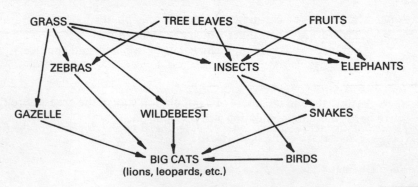

⇒ C1/18

14

G5 *[State 2 ways in which energy can be lost from a food web.]*

When a plant or animal is eaten by another animal, only about 10% of the energy passed on is turned into new animal tissue. This huge energy loss at each stage in a food chain (about 90%) is due to food (chemical) energy being turned into, or lost as;

(a) heat energy

(b) movement energy

(c) energy lost in solid waste (the indigestible material).

Summary

Energy lost from a food web

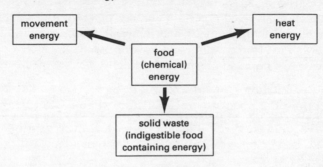

Note: Some solid waste may be used as an energy source by other organisms, e.g. fungi and bacteria, but this will also be lost as heat energy eventually.

$\Rightarrow$ C2/19

Population Growth

G6 *[State that the growth rate of a population depends on birth rate and death rate.]*

If we assume that all members of a population stay in the area where they were born, then the population size depends on;

(a) how many are being born (**birth rate**)
and

(b) how many are dying   (**death rate**).

If the birth rate is more than the death rate, the population will **increase**.
If the birth rate is less than the death rate, the population will **decrease**.

What can limit the growth of a population?

G7 *[State 3 factors which can limit the growth of a population.]*

There are many ways in which growth of a population may be affected. The main factors limiting its growth are

lack of food   lack of space
disease   predators.

If there is a **lack of food**, weaker individuals may die of starvation and fewer young may be produced.

Lack of living space may also reduce the number of young produced, as many animals need a certain amount of space for breeding. Individuals not having enough space may leave the population and try their luck elsewhere. Overcrowding and lack of space may increase the amount of **disease** in a population which may kill the weaker members.

As a population grows, there will be more food for its natural **predators**. therefore the population of predators will increase. Increased predation will decrease the population again.

$$\Rightarrow C3/19 + C4/20$$

G8 *[State that competition occurs when organisms have a need for the same resources.]*

In all the examples given above (G7), animals (and often plants) are competing with others in the same population and in other populations for their basic needs: food, space, etc. (Examples in a plant population: sunlight, water, minerals from soil.)

Some examples of the effects of competition

G9 *[Describe some effects of competition.]*

Organism	Resource competed for	Effect of Competition
barley	light	plants grow tall to obtain maximum light
barley	soil minerals	plants may be stunted or yellow if not enough minerals for all
gannet	breeding space	those not obtaining a nest site will not mate
gannet	food	youngest chicks may not survive if food is scarce

16

Nutrient Cycles

G10 *[Explain why re-cycling of nutrients is important to the organisms in an ecosystem.]*

As well as energy, living things need minerals (e.g. nitrates and phosphates) in order to stay alive. Plants get these nutrients from the soil. Animals get them from eating plants or other animals (all originally coming from the soil).

Within an ecosystem, there is a limited supply of these nutrients. Plants are continually using them up and if they were not replaced, the soil would soon be unable to support any further plant growth. Fortunately, when plants and animals die, their remains are broken down by bacteria and fungi in the soil (**decomposers**) and the mineral nutrients are put back into the soil once again. Also, animal excretion returns nutrients back to the soil.

Summary

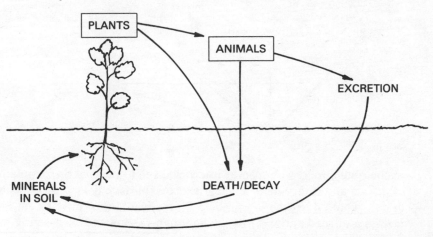

⇒ C5/21

17

CREDIT LEVEL

Removing an organism from a food web

C1 *[Explain how removing one organism from a food web could affect the other organisms.]*

Removing all the thrushes from the following simple food chain

GRASS ──────►SNAILS ──────►THRUSHES

would result in more snails surviving, which in turn would mean more grass being eaten.

Unexpected results may sometimes arise from the removal of an organism from a food web:

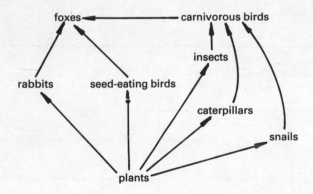

In the above food web, use of insecticide might remove the populations of insects and caterpillars. The carnivorous birds, having only snails now to eat, would decrease in numbers. Foxes would now have to eat more rabbits and seed-eating birds, so although rabbits and seed-eating birds might seem unlikely to be affected by insecticides, they may be, indirectly.

18

Pyramid of numbers and pyramid of biomass

C2 *[Explain what is meant by the terms pyramid of numbers and pyramid of biomass.]*

A pyramid of numbers shows that the number or organisms at each level of a food chain decreases at each stage because of the large energy loss.

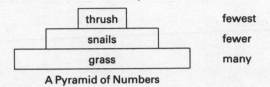

A Pyramid of Numbers

The pyramid of biomass is similar except that it represents the mass of the organisms (not number) at each level in a food web. It is usually (although not always) the same shape as the pyramid of numbers.

Population Graphs

C3 *[Describe the shape of the growth curve of a population, under ideal conditions.]*

1. Steady population (birth rate = death rate).

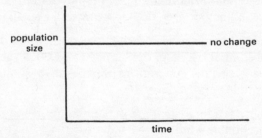

2. Population increasing under ideal conditions (birth rate much greater than death rate).

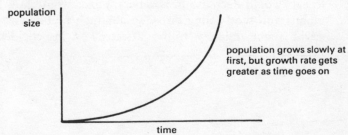

19

C4 *[Explain the shape of the growth curve of a population, under ideal conditions.]*

The growth curve of a population under ideal conditions has three stages.

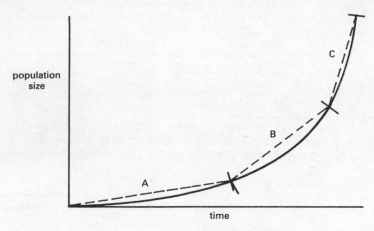

Stage A   The population is small. Ideal conditions mean that death rate is low, but even doubling of the population only causes a small rise in number, e.g. double 4 = 8, still a small number.

Stage B   The population has reached the stage when doubling causes a substantial rise, e.g. double 4000 = 8000, a substantial number. Also, several generations will be alive at the same time, all reproducing.

Stage C   There is a huge increase in population size in a very short time, e.g. double 4 million = 8 million.

Nitrogen Cycle

C5 *[Describe the sequence of processes in the nitrogen cycle.]*

Nitrogen is an essential element for plants and animals, as it is necessary for the production of protein. It is re-cycled by the action of bacteria.

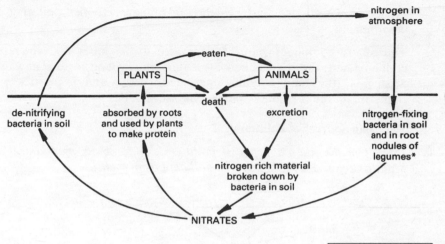

21

SUB-TOPIC (c) — Control and Management

GENERAL LEVEL

Pollution

G1 *[State that pollution affects air, fresh water, sea and land.]*

Wherever we go, we find evidence of human activities polluting our environment.

The **air** is no longer pure; **fresh water** lochs, lakes and rivers are contaminated; the **sea** has become a dumping ground for our unwanted waste and the **land** contains man-made waste and impurities even thousands of miles from the nearest industrial areas.

The Main Sources of Pollution

G2 *[State that the main sources of pollution are domestic, agricultural and industrial, giving an example of a pollutant from each.]*

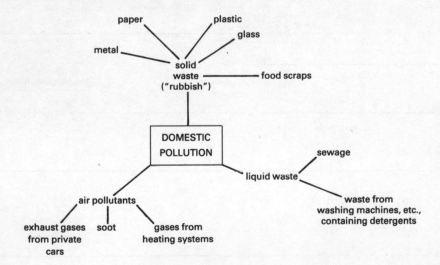

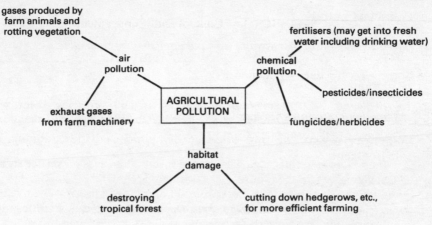

gases produced by
farm animals and
rotting vegetation

air
pollution

exhaust gases
from farm machinery

**AGRICULTURAL
POLLUTION**

chemical
pollution

fertilisers (may get into fresh
water including drinking water)

pesticides/insecticides

fungicides/herbicides

habitat
damage

destroying
tropical forest

cutting down hedgerows, etc.,
for more efficient farming

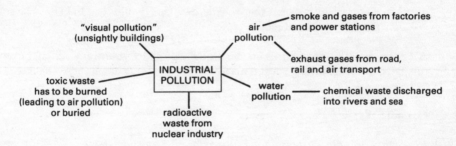

"visual pollution"
(unsightly buildings)

air
pollution

smoke and gases from factories
and power stations

**INDUSTRIAL
POLLUTION**

toxic waste
has to be burned
(leading to air pollution)
or buried

exhaust gases from road,
rail and air transport

water
pollution

chemical waste discharged
into rivers and sea

radioactive
waste from
nuclear industry

⇒ C1/26

Pollution Control

G3 *[Give an example of one way in which pollution may be controlled.]*

Some ways of reducing pollution are:

1. *Reducing the use of harmful substances* and replacing them with "environmentally friendly" ones, e.g. using aerosol propellants that do no damage to the ozone layer.

2. *Re-cycling materials,* e.g., glass, paper, metal. This saves raw materials and energy.

3. *Cleaning up discharges to the environment,* e.g. using catalytic converters to clean up car exhausts; "scrubbers" to clean up discharges from factory chimneys.

4. *Make industrial processes more efficient.* This would lead to better use of rare raw materials and reduce waste.

All of these pollution controls can be brought about by **voluntary** action, but if this fails, government **legislation** may be needed to bring about these changes.

Organic Waste

G4 *[State that organic waste is a food source for micro-organisms.]*

Organic waste is composed of chemicals containing carbon or material of animal or plant origin, which has been released into the environment.

Most forms of organic waste can be used as food by micro-organisms such as bacteria and fungi.

Examples of organic waste:	sewage
	oil spills
	sugar solution and other organic chemicals
	from industrial processes
	blood from slaughter houses.

G5 *[Describe the effect of increased numbers of micro-organisms on the oxygen available to other organisms.]*

Most of the micro-organisms that use organic waste as food need oxygen as we do. In polluted water, growth of micro-organisms can lead to rapid use of the dissolved oxygen which is needed by the other water dwelling organisms.

$\Rightarrow$ C2/27 + C3/28

Management of Resources

G6 *[Give two examples of poor management of natural resources and suggest possible improvements.]*

G7 *[Describe how the effect of poor management of natural resources can lead to problems.]*

Examples of poor management	Problems arising	Possible improvements
1. Destroying rain forest for short term gain from cash crops.	Loss of species. Possible climatic disturbance.	Protect remaining rain forest. Re-plant native hardwoods. Provide financial incentives to stop growth of cash crops.
2. Uncontrolled overfishing	Destruction of fish stocks (e.g. North Sea herring).	Regulate fishing effort. Encourage catching of little used species.
3. Overgrazing of grassland	Soil erosion. Loss of fertile top soil.	Rotate areas used for grazing.
4. Over use of chemicals for *(a)* pest control *(b)* improving soil fertility	Chemicals may harm other organisms in the food web. Nutrients can pollute waterways.	Reduce dependance on chemicals by encouraging more natural farming practices.

$\Rightarrow$ C4/28

CREDIT LEVEL

C1 *[Explain an undesirable effect of using (a) fossil fuels and (b) nuclear power as energy sources.]*

(a) Fossil fuels

Fossil fuels, i.e. coal, oil (including petrol) and gas, all release undesirable chemicals into the environment when they burn.

These include:

sulphur dioxide	can lead to acid rain
oxides of nitrogen	can cause an increase in ozone, which is desirable in the upper atmosphere but damaging to crops at ground level.
carbon monoxide	poisonous
lead (car exhausts)	known to cause brain damage.

(b) Nuclear power

As the accident at Chernobyl in the former U.S.S.R. showed, a serious fault in a nuclear power station can have a catastrophic effect on the environment over a very wide area. Nuclear material taken into the food chain may take thousands of years to disappear and may cause cancer in some of those exposed to it.

The effect of pollution on a number of species

C2 *[Explain how organic waste pollution can affect the numbers of micro-organisms and hence oxygen concentration and numbers of species.]*

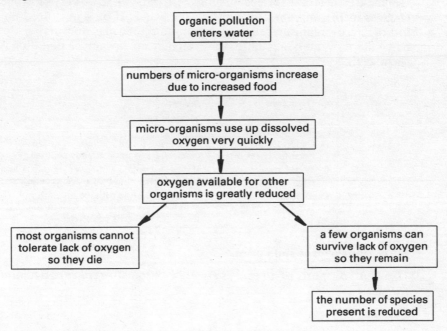

organic pollution
enters water

↓

numbers of micro-organisms increase
due to increased food

↓

micro-organisms use up dissolved
oxygen very quickly

↓

oxygen available for other
organisms is greatly reduced

↙   ↘

most organisms cannot
tolerate lack of oxygen
so they die

a few organisms can
survive lack of oxygen
so they remain

↓

the number of species
present is reduced

Indicator Organisms

C3 *[State what is meant by "indicator species" and explain how they are affected by changing oxygen concentrations.]*

Certain freshwater invertebrate animals are known to be very sensitive to changes in the amount of oxygen in the water. If oxygen is used up by lots of micro-organisms feeding on pollution, they may not survive. So by being there or not being there, they can indicate how much pollution is in the water.

Examples:

Organisms	*Indication*
A Stone fly nymph May fly nymph	These animals only occur in **unpolluted** water.
B Caddis fly larvae Freshwater shrimp	If these are found without any group A animals, the water is **slightly polluted**
C Water louse Blood worm	If these are found without any group A and B animals, the water has **serious pollution**
D Tubifex worm Rat-tailed maggot	If these are found without any of the animals in groups A, B or C, it means that the water is **heavily polluted**.

Farm Management and Forestry

C4 *[Explain how parts of an ecosystem are controlled in either agriculture or forestry.]*

Farming

The parts of a farm ecosystem that a farmer must control are:
1. Soil fertility, i.e. adequate essential minerals.
2. What plants are grown, i.e. only the desired plants — no competition from weeds.
3. Disease causing organisms.

Management methods

In the past *crop rotation* was the only management method available. Crop rotation means growing different crops in successive years in a particular field, e.g.

Year 1   barley
Year 2   sugar beet
Year 3   clover (which replaces soil nitrates)
Year 4   barley again

This system does not allow persistent weeds or disease causing organisms to build up in the soil.

At the present time a combination of simple crop rotation plus agricultural chemicals is used.

Chemicals used:

(a) artificial fertilisers (nitrates, phosphates and potassium);

(b) insecticides to kill insects which may eat crops or carry disease;

(c) fungicides to prevent fungal diseases;

(d) herbicides to kill weed species.

Forestry

In addition to the factors of the ecosystem managed by farmers, foresters have a number of other factors to manage.

As forestry is often carried out on poor quality soil in exposed sites, seedlings are usually grown in protected *nurseries*, then *transplanted* out. Planting sites may need *deep ploughing* and drainage. Young trees need protection against *animal damage*, in particular by deer.

Due to the long growing period (70 to 80 years for conifers, 100+ years for hardwood), trees are planted close together then *thinned* at intervals, leaving the strongest specimens. *Fire* is another environmental hazard that must be managed by foresters.

TOPIC 2 INVESTIGATING CELLS

SUB-TOPIC (a) – Investigating Living Cells

GENERAL LEVEL

The "Bricks of Life"

G1 *[State that cells are the basic units of living things.]*

With the aid of a microscope, it can be seen that all life, from bacteria to the largest plants and animals, are all built up of common units ("building blocks") called cells. Cells are usually so small that they have to magnified many times in order to be seen. The differences in size of living things depends largely on the **number** of cells in their body.

Unicellular organisms are organisms consisting of a single cell, e.g. bacteria, *Pleurococcus* (plant) and *Amoeba* (animal).

Very small objects such as bacteria are measured in μm (microns).
1μm = 1/1000 mm.

Simple multicellular animals (e.g. flatworms) and plants (e.g. moss), although very small, consist of hundreds of thousands of cells. Larger multicellular animals and plants consist of many millions of cells. Generally, these cells range in size from 10 μm up to 200 μm.

Observing Cells

G2 *[Explain the purpose of staining plant and animal cells.]*

Cells are viewed on a microscope by pasing light through the specimen, then magnifying the image. The specimen must therefore be **thin** to allow light to pass through and ideally, only a single layer of cells thick.

Some parts of cells are almost transparent and so they may appear almost invisible. In order to provide **contrast**, stain is added to the specimen. Some parts will absorb the stain better than other parts, so they will show up against unstained areas.

Two common stains

Material	Stain	Effect
plant cells (e.g. onion epidermis)	iodine	stains nuclei brown
animal cells (e.g. human cheek cells)	methylene blue	stains nuclei blue

Special stains are sometimes used which can show up other cell structures, or even certain chemicals in the cells.

Structure of cells

G3 *[Describe the structure of a typical plant cell and a typical animal cell and list the differences between them.]*

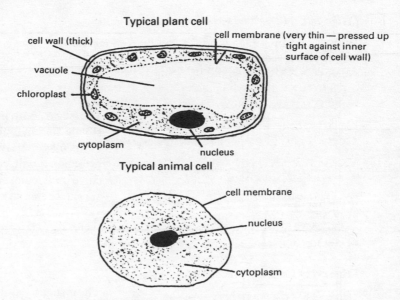

Differences between plant and animal cells

	Plant cells	*Animal cells*
1. cell wall	always	never
2. large central vacuole	most	never
3. chloroplasts	some cells (parts exposed to light only)	never

As can be seen from the above table, the surest way of distinguishing between a plant and an animal cell is by the presence or absence of a cell wall.

(**Note**:   The functions of the various parts of the cell are not dealt with here. This is covered in later sub-topics.)

31

SUB-TOPIC (b) — Investigating Diffusion

GENERAL LEVEL

High to Low

G1 *[State that a substance will diffuse from an area of high concentration to an area of low concentration (of that substance).]*

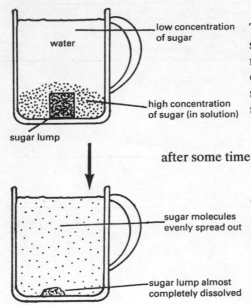

The sugar lump in the cup will slowly dissolve and the water molecules, moving in all directions, will bump into the sugar molecules and gradually spread them out.

after some time

The sugar molecules have **diffused** from an area of **high** sugar concentration to an area of **low** sugar concentration. Eventually, the concentration of sugar molecules will be the same everywhere in the cup.

Substances can also diffuse through a gas, e.g.

A smelly gas escaping from a chemistry laboratory (high concentration) will spread by diffusion to other parts of the school (low concentration).

Diffusion and Cells

G2 *[Give examples of substances which enter and leave the cell by diffusion, e.g. dissolved food, oxygen and carbon dioxide.]*

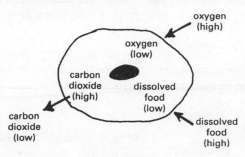

Oxygen and dissolved food are raw materials and will diffuse into an animal cell. Carbon dioxide is a waste product and will diffuse out of an animal cell. (N.B. Green plant cells in sunlight may behave differently — see *World of Plants* page 68.)

⇒ C1/36

Diffusion through the Cell Membrane

G3 *[State that the cell membrane controls the passage of substances in and out of the cell.]*

Put very simply, a cell membrane has holes (or pores) of a certain size. Small molecules may pass through these pores, but large molecules may not.

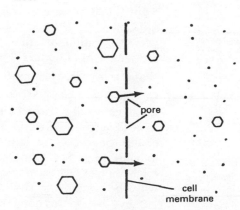

The glucose and sucrose molecules are both at a higher concentration on the left of the membrane so will move from left to right by diffusion. The glucose molecules are small enough to pass through the pores in the membrane, but the sucrose molecules are too large.

⬡ = a sucrose molecule
○ = a glucose molecule
• = a water molecule

33

Osmosis — the diffusion of water through the membrane

G4   *[Explain that osmosis is a "special case" of the diffusion of water.]*

Water molecules are very small and can pass through the pores in the cell membrane with no difficulty. This movement of water through a cell membrane is called *osmosis*.

Plant and animal cells (or even whole plants and whole animals) can gain or lose water by osmosis. The movement of water into or out of a cell depends on the concentration of the solution surrounding the cell.

A   *Cells in a weak (very watery) solution*

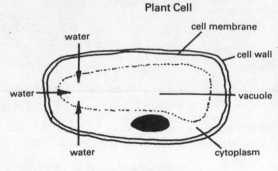

Plant Cell

Plant cell in water or dilute solution (e.g. when plant has adequate water available).

Water moves in by *osmosis*.

Cell swells up (becomes *turgid*) but cannot burst because of tough cell wall. This is desirable in plants as it makes the whole plant more rigid.

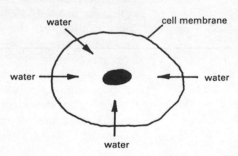

Animal Cell

Animal cell in water or dilute solution (e.g. when blood becomes diluted due to drinking a lot of liquid).

Water moves in by *osmosis*.

Cell swells up and without a tough cell wall to protect it, it is in danger of bursting. This could be very serious in animals (e.g. red blood cells might burst) but excess water will be removed by the kidneys to stop this happening (see sub-topic "Water and Waste" page 86).

B   *Cells in a strong solution (less water)*

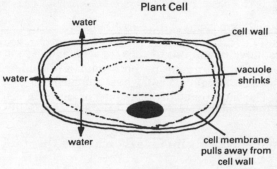

Plant Cell

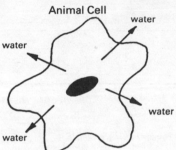

Animal Cell

Plant cell in strong solution (e.g. when plant has lost too much water).

Water moves out by *osmosis*.

Vacuole shrinks, membrane pulls away from wall and cell becomes flaccid. The plant will wilt.

Animal cell in strong solution (e.g. when blood becomes too concentrated due to sweating).

Water moves out by *osmosis*.

Cell shrinks and it may not work properly. The animal suffers from dehydration.

These examples show that water moves from one side of a membrane where there is plenty of water, to the other side where there is less water. Osmosis is therefore a special type of diffusion of water, through a membrane.

⇒ C2/36 + C3/36

35

CREDIT LEVEL

Diffusion in whole organisms

C1 *[Explain the importance of diffusion to organisms.]*

In the same way that gases move in and out of cells, oxygen and carbon dioxide also move in and out of whole organisms, both animals (including humans) and plants.

In small organisms (e.g. amoeba, bacteria, etc.), gas diffuses in and out through the cell membrane.

In larger organisms, there are special organs for gas exchange. These are needed as diffusion would be too slow.

Organism	Gas Exchange 'Organ'
amoeba	cell membrane
tree	leaves
fish	gills
cow	lungs

C2 *[Explain osmosis in terms of a selectively permeable membrane and of a concentration gradient.]*

C3 *[Explain osmosis in terms of "water concentration".]*

To help understand diffusion of water, try to imagine high and low **water concentration**, e.g.

a 20% salt solution (A in diagram below) must be 20% salt and **80% water** and
a   5% salt solution (B in diagram below) must be 5% salt and **95% water**.

So we can think of solution A as having a low water concentration and solution B as having a high water concentration.

Now imagine these two solutions (A and B) separated by a membrane.

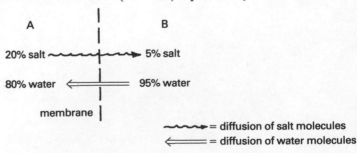

Water molecules, being smaller than salt molecules, can move through the membrane faster. Very large molecules cannot pass through the membrane at all. Because of this, membranes are referred to as *selectively permeable*. The difference in water concentration on the opposite sides of the membrane causes what is called a *concentration gradient*. (Remember, gradient = slope. Things will roll down a slope from high to low, so water moves down a water concentration gradient from **high** water concentration to **low** concentration.) Concentration gradient can be used to describe differences in concentration of other substances apart from water.

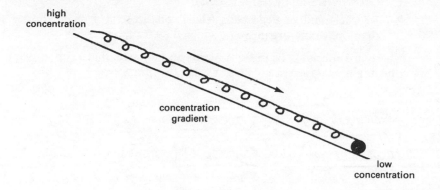

SUB-TOPIC (c) — Investigating Cell Division

GENERAL LEVEL

Why do cells divide?

G1 *[State that cell division is a means of increasing the number of cells in an organism.]*

New cells are needed by multi-cellular plants and animals for two purposes.

1. Growth (for an increase in size).
2. Replacement of dead cells (most cells live for a much shorter time than the whole organism of which they form a part).

There are special cells in both plants and animals that keep growing and dividing to produce new cells for these two purposes.

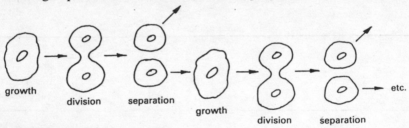

The importance of the nucleus

G2 *[State that the nucleus of the cell controls cell activities, including cell division.]*

The nucleus is the control centre of a cell. Inside the nucleus are a number of thin, threadlike objects called *chromosomes*. The number of chromosomes is the same in every cell of an organism's body. Each species has a characteristic **chromosome number**. The human chromosome number is 46 (i.e. there are 46 chromosomes in the nuclei of all our cells).

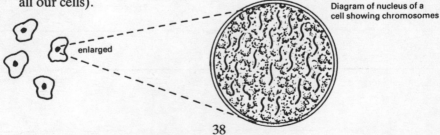

Diagram of nucleus of a cell showing chromosomes

38

The chromosomes carry a complete set of information relating to the particular individual in whose cells they are. Everything that a cell does, including cell division, is controlled by the information on the chromosomes. When a cell divides, it is essential that **each** of the two cells resulting has a **complete** set of instructions. That is why nuclear division must take place before a cell can split into two daughter cells.

Mitosis

G3 *[State that each of the two cells produced by cell division has a complete set of chromosomes and the same information.]*

If a human cell has 46 chromosomes, when it divides, the daughter cells must also have 46 each. But not just **any** 46. They must both have complete and identical sets.

Each one of the 46 chromosomes is copied and separated so that one of the copies goes into each daughter cell. This process of **copying** and **separating** the chromosomes, followed by division of the cytoplasm is called *mitosis*.

Summary of mitosis

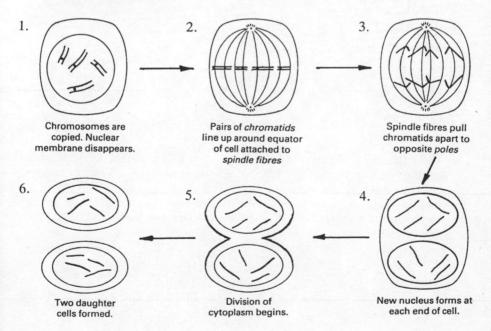

1. Chromosomes are copied. Nuclear membrane disappears.

2. Pairs of *chromatids* line up around equator of cell attached to *spindle fibres*

3. Spindle fibres pull chromatids apart to opposite *poles*

4. New nucleus forms at each end of cell.

5. Division of cytoplasm begins.

6. Two daughter cells formed.

N.B.   *Chromatids*   — The name given to the copied chromosomes, still joined together, before separation.

Spindle fibres — fibres of cytoplasm that pull the pairs of chromatids apart.

Poles   — the opposite ends of the cell.

⇒ C1/41 + C2/42

G4 *[Identify the correct sequence of stages of mitosis from a series of drawings or diagrams.]*

Using the information in G3, sort out the following jumbled up diagrams of mitosis into the correct order.

A

B

C

D
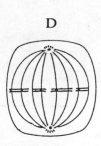

E

F
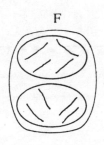

CREDIT LEVEL

The main events in cell division

C1 *[Describe the stages of mitosis.]*

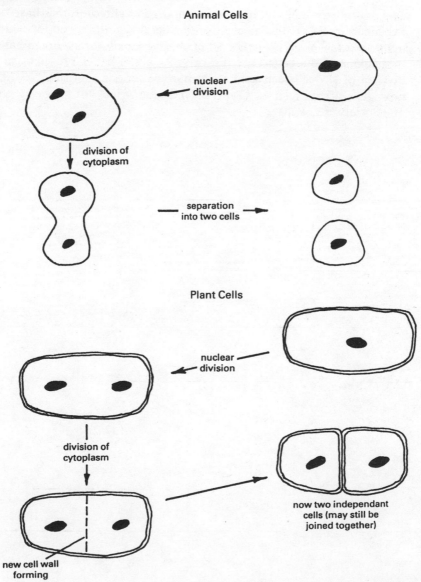

Animal Cells

nuclear division

division of cytoplasm

separation into two cells

Plant Cells

nuclear division

division of cytoplasm

new cell wall forming

now two independant cells (may still be joined together)

41

Maintaining the chromosome complement

C2 *[Explain why it is important that the chromosome complement of daughter cells in multi-cellular organisms is maintained.]*

The reasons for the doubling and separating of chromosomes have been explained in G4. If the mechanism breaks down and a cell inherits too many, too few or an incorrect set of chromosomes, it may not behave as it should and the cells may die or grow abnormally. Problems in the division of sex cells can lead to even more serious abnormalities in the next generation, such as Down's Syndrome. (See sub-topic "Genetics and Society" page 131.)

SUB-TOPIC (d) — Investigating Enzymes

GENERAL LEVEL

(**Note:** In this sub-topic, the order of Learning Outcomes G1 and G2, as printed in the syllabus, has been reversed.)

What is a catalyst?

G1 *[Explain the meaning of the term "catalyst".]*

A catalyst is a chemical substance which helps a chemical reaction to take place, but is not used up in the reaction itself, e.g.

$$\text{chemical A} + \text{chemical B} \xrightarrow{\text{catalyst X}} \text{chemical C}$$

Chemicals A and B might react under conditions of high temperature and pressure, but the addition of catalyst X causes the reaction to take place at lower temperatures and pressures.

Enzymes — biological catalysts

G2 *[Explain why enzymes are required for the functions of living cells.]*

Thousands of reactions like the one above (A + B → C) take place in living tissue. Most are controlled by catalysts made by the cells themselves. These biological catalysts are called *enzymes*.

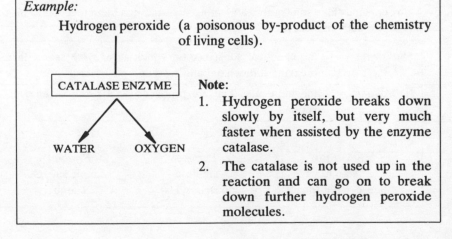

Example:

Hydrogen peroxide (a poisonous by-product of the chemistry of living cells).

CATALASE ENZYME

WATER   OXYGEN

Note:

1. Hydrogen peroxide breaks down slowly by itself, but very much faster when assisted by the enzyme catalase.

2. The catalase is not used up in the reaction and can go on to break down further hydrogen peroxide molecules.

Amylase, a "breaking down" enzyme ...

G3 *[Give an example of an enzyme involved in the chemical breakdown of a substance.]*

The enzyme *amylase* is found in the digestive system of animals and in the seeds and food storage organs of plants. Amylase is responsible for the breakdown of large starch molecules into smaller sugar molecules.

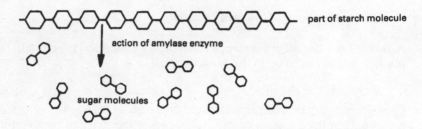

This is only one example of an enzyme causing the breakdown of large molecules into smaller ones. Others will be met in later chapters.

... and potato phosphorylase, a "joining together" enzyme

G4 *[Give an example of an enzyme involved in synthesis.]*

Many enzymes take small substrate* molecules and join them together to make larger product** molecules.

---

*Substrate = the chemical substance on which an enzyme acts, either breaking it down or building it up.

**Product = the molecules that are produced as a result of enzyme action.

e.g.

Substrate	Enzyme	Product
starch	amylase	simple sugars
glucose-1-phosphate	phosphorylase	starch

44

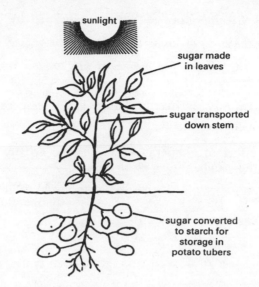

Sugar made in the leaves of a potato plant (see Topic "World of Plants" page 58) has to be turned into starch for storage in the underground tubers, i.e. potatoes. This is done by the enzyme *potato phosphorylase* joining together molecules of the sugar *glucose-1-phosphate*.

$$\text{glucose-1-phosphate} \xrightarrow[\text{enzyme}]{\text{phosphorylase}} \text{starch}$$

$$\boxed{\Rightarrow \text{C1/47}}$$

The chemical nature of enzymes

G5 *[State that enzymes are proteins.]*

All enzymes are *protein* molecules. Acting as enzymes is one of the most important functions of proteins in living cells. The fact that enzymes are proteins explains their responses to temperature and pH covered in G6 and G7.

The effect of temperature and pH on enzyme activity

G6 *[Describe the effect of temperature on enzyme activity.]*

G7 *[Describe the effect of a range of pH on the activity of pepsin and catalase.]*

Enzymes are very sensitive to changes in cell temperature and pH.

1. *Temperature*

   The effect of temperature on enzyme activity, i.e. how fast it is working, can be shown by a graph.

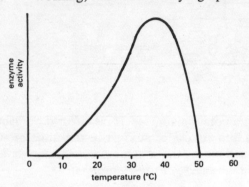

The graph shows that at low temperatures, the enzyme works very slowly, then speeds up as the temperature rises. In the case of human enzymes, most work fastest at about body temperature (37 °C). As temperature increases further, enzyme activity quickly decreases and stops altogether above approximately 50 °C.

2. *pH*

   Every enzyme works best at a particular pH. The following graph shows how two human enzymes prefer different pH conditions.

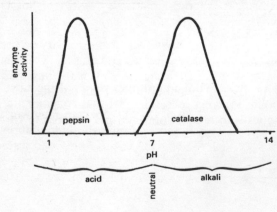

The graph shows that pepsin (a protein digesting enzyme secreted by the stomach) works best in acidic conditions. Catalase (see G2) works best in alkaline conditions.

The ability of pepsin to break down a protein such as albumen (egg white) is much reduced if the pH is not acidic enough.

⇒ C2/47

46

CREDIT LEVEL

Enzymes are "specific"

C1 *[Explain the term "specific" as applied to enzymes and their substrates.]*

A key will only open a lock with a matching shape. In the same way, an enzyme molecule has a particular shape and will only affect substrate molecules with a matching shape. The enzyme is said to be **specific** to that substrate.

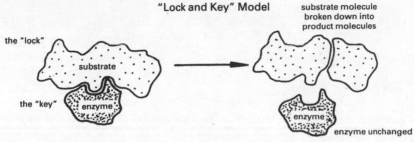

"Lock and Key" Model

(N.B. This example is of a "breaking down" enzyme in action, e.g. amylase. A "joining together" enzyme, e.g. phosphorylase, works in reverse.)

Optimum conditions for enzyme action

C2 *[Explain the term "optimum" as applied to the activity of enzymes.]*

The graphs in G6 and G7 show that enzymes have a particular temperature and pH at which they work best. These "best" conditions are called the **optimum** conditions for that particular enzyme, e.g.

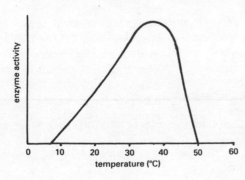

The peak enzyme activity occurs at a temperature of 37 °C. Thus in this case, 37 °C is the optimum temperature of this enzyme.

Note that an enzyme may work within a range of temperatures and pH, but activity decreases the further conditions move away from the optimum.

SUB-TOPIC (e) – Investigating Aerobic Respiration

GENERAL LEVEL

The need for energy

G1 *[State three reasons why living cells need energy.]*

Living cells need energy for:

1.   cell division
2.   cell growth
3.   movement (muscle cells)
4.   making certain chemical reactions work.

The need for oxygen

$\Rightarrow$ C1/50

G2 *[State that cells need oxygen to release energy from food during aerobic respiration.]*

Burning a piece of food can show its energy content. As food burns, it uses up oxygen. Without oxygen, nothing will burn.

The release of energy from food inside a cell also needs oxygen.

FOOD + OXYGEN ⟶ {ENERGY} + WASTE PRODUCTS

The release of energy from food takes place only inside cells and is called *cellular respiration.*

As the process uses oxygen, it is referred to as **aerobic** *respiration.*
       (*Aerobic* = with "air" – as in **aero**batics, but here, specifically with oxygen.)

Summary

G3 *[Describe aerobic respiration in terms of a word equation.]*

FOOD (e.g. glucose) + OXYGEN ⟶ ENERGY + CARBON DIOXIDE + WATER

The waste products from aerobic respiration

G4 *[State that the carbon dioxide given off by cells during tissue respiration has come from food.]*

G5 *[State that heat energy may be released from cells during respiration.]*

Carbohydrates, proteins and fats, the three main types of food that are used by living cells, all contain the elements *carbon* and *oxygen*. As energy is released from these foods inside the cell, the carbon and oxygen are released in the form of *carbon dioxide* gas.

Some of the energy released from food during respiration is in the form of heat energy. It is possible to tell the difference between living cells and dead cells by measuring the heat given off by the living cells, e.g. germinating peas are warmer than dead peas.

$\Rightarrow$ C2/50

CREDIT LEVEL

The energy content of food

C1 *[State that fats contain more chemical energy per gram than carbohydrates or proteins.]*

The energy contained in food can be estimated by burning. The heat given off by the burning food sample heats a known volume of water and the rise of temperature of the water is measured.

1 g of carbohydrate } gives off approximately 20 "units" of heat
1 g of protein

1 g of fat (or oil)   gives off approximately 40 "units" of heat.

This shows that fats contain approximately twice as much energy as the same mass of carbohydrates or proteins.

Fats and carbohydrates are used as our main sources of energy.

Energy and cell metabolism

C2 *[Explain the importance of energy released from food during respiration to the metabolism of cells.]*

All the chemical reactions taking place inside a cell are known together as *cell metabolism*. Many of these reactions, without which the cell cannot survive, need energy to make them work.

$$A + B \longrightarrow \text{nothing happens}$$

$$\text{but } A + B \xrightarrow{\text{+ energy}} C$$

The energy to make these reactions take place comes from the stored chemical energy in food.

SUB-TOPIC (a) — Introducing Plants

GENERAL LEVEL

Variety in the Plant Kingdom

G1 *[Give examples of advantages of there being a wide variety of plants.]*

G2 *[Describe three specialised uses of plants.]*

Humans make many different uses of plants. This variety of uses is possible because such a wide variety of plant types exist.

Here are a few examples:

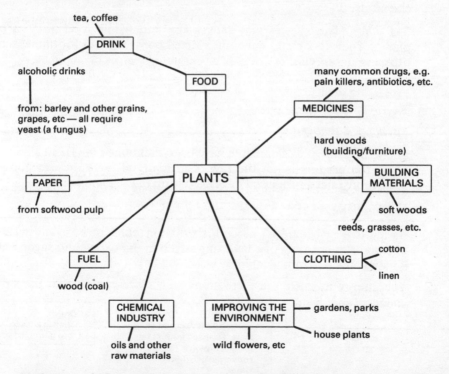

Medicines, clothing and *paper* are three specialised uses of plants. They are specialised because the plants used as raw materials must be processed or treated in some way before the product is produced.

⇒ C1/52 + C2/52 + C3/53

CREDIT LEVEL

Extinction of plant species

C1 *[Explain possible consequences to humans and other animals of a reduction in the variety of plant species.]*

Some plant species are being used up at such a rate that they may not survive. Certain hardwood trees used in the building and furniture industries are in danger of extinction.

Many other plant species are not used directly by humans, but their loss would mean a reduction in the "storehouse" of plant material which may prove in the future to hold new food species, new drugs and new chemicals.

Yet other plant species may play a key part in the food webs of our planet. Their loss could have unexpected consequences for humans and other animal species.

Processing plants

C2 *[Describe a production or refining process, e.g. malting barley, rape seed, raspberries, timber.]*

Many specialised uses of plants have been mentioned in G1. In almost all cases, the **product** is not the raw plant material (with the exception of some foods) but a processed or refined form of the plant material.

Malting barley

Barley is a raw material used in the manufacture of beer and whisky. Malting is the process of converting starch in the barley into sugar which is then converted into alcohol by yeast.

The malting process

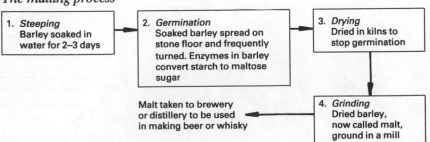

1. *Steeping*
   Barley soaked in water for 2–3 days

2. *Germination*
   Soaked barley spread on stone floor and frequently turned. Enzymes in barley convert starch to maltose sugar

3. *Drying*
   Dried in kilns to stop germination

4. *Grinding*
   Dried barley, now called malt, ground in a mill

Malt taken to brewery or distillery to be used in making beer or whisky

New uses of plants

C3 *[Describe two potential uses of plants or plant products, e.g. new medicines, sources of fuel, oils.]*

1. *New medicines*

   Many new drugs, particularly antibiotics, have been developed from chemicals obtained from plants.

2. *New fuels*

   Fermentation, the action of yeast on sugar, produces alcohol which burns and can therefore be used as a fuel. Sugar comes from plants such as sugar cane and sugar beet.

   This alcohol (or an alcohol/petrol mixture called "gasohol") can be used to power car engines.

   Advantage: Plant material is renewable, unlike oil which is a non-renewable fuel.

   Disadvantage: Alcohol on its own only works well as an alternative to petrol in hot climates. In cold climates, petrol must still be added to help the fuel to burn at low temperatures.

SUB-TOPIC (b) — Growing Plants

GENERAL LEVEL

Structure of a seed

G1 *[Describe the functions of three main parts of a seed, i.e. seed coat, embryo and food store.]*

Most plants begin life as a seed. The structure of a seed protects and feeds the embryo plant inside.

Inside a broad bean seed

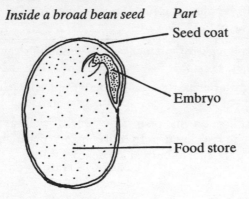

Part	Function
Seed coat	Protects the embryo plant and its food store until conditions are suitable for germination (growth).
Embryo	The future plant. Part will develop into roots and part into stem and leaves.
Food store	Food (starch) to keep the embryo alive inside the seed and during germination until the new leaves can make more food.

Conditions for germination

G2 *[Describe the effect of temperature and the availability of water and oxygen on germination.]*

Germination is the process in which the embryo plant inside a seed begins to grow. Roots grow down into the soil and a shoot grows up through the soil to emerge into the light.

Seeds need three environmental conditions to be suitable before they can germinate.

1. *Temperature.* If temperature is too low, germination is prevented. (If it were not, frost could kill the emerging seedling.)

2. *Water.* Water is needed to soften the seed coat and start the growth of the embryo. (Dry seeds in a packet will not germinate, even if all the other conditions are right.)

54

3. *Oxygen*. During germination, the growing embryo needs much more oxygen than it did while it was dormant inside the seed. Insufficient oxygen will prevent germination.

$\Rightarrow$ C1/59

Flower structure

G3 *[Describe the functions of the parts of flowers, i.e. sepal, petal, stamen, anther, stigma, ovary and nectary.]*

Inside a simple flower	*Part*	*Function*
	1. Flower stalk	supports flower
	2. Sepal	protects flower bud before opening
	3. Petal	attracts insects/protects other flower parts
	4. Anther	produces pollen, the male sex cells. Together with its stalk, known as a stamen
	5. Stigma	sticky platform on to which insects deposit pollen from other flowers
	6. Ovary	produces ovules, the female sex cells. This part later forms the seed
	7. Nectary	produces sugary nectar to attract insects.

Pollination

G4 *[Describe methods of pollination.]*

1. *Insect Pollinated Flowers*. (Brightly coloured, scented flowers with nectar. All features which attract insects.)

    An insect enters one flower in search of nectar and brushes against the ripe anthers. Pollen sticks to the insect's body. The insect flies to another flower and if the stigma is ripe, the pollen from the first flower will stick to it, so pollinating the flower.

2. *Wind Pollinated Flowers.* (Small dull flowers with no nectar, e.g. grasses.)

Large numbers of light pollen grains are produced by large anthers hanging down outside the flower. The pollen grains are carried away in the wind. Some may be caught on the large feathery stigma hanging out of another flower, so pollinating the flower.

⇒ C2/60

Fertilisation and Fruit Formation

G5 *[Describe fertilisation and fruit formation.]*

After pollination, the male and female sex cells (gametes) are still some distance apart.

Fertilisation of the ovule

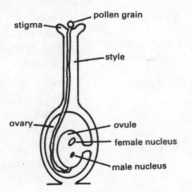

A tube grows from the pollen grain down through the style and into the ovary. It enters an ovule and the male nucleus from the pollen grain enters the ovule and fertilises the female gamete.

After fertilisation, the fruit develops as follows:

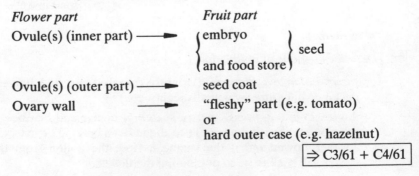

Flower part	Fruit part
Ovule(s) (inner part) ⟶	{ embryo and food store } seed
Ovule(s) (outer part) ⟶	seed coat
Ovary wall ⟶	"fleshy" part (e.g. tomato) or hard outer case (e.g. hazelnut)

⇒ C3/61 + C4/61

56

Artificial propagation

G6 *[Describe ways of propagating flowering plants artificially by cuttings and grafting.]*

1. *Cuttings*

    (i) The stem is cut just below a leaf or leaf bud.

    (ii) The cut stem is dusted with hormone powder to encourage growth of new roots.

    (iii) The cutting is potted up in damp compost.

    (iv) After a few weeks, new roots develop and the cutting is now an independant plant.

2. *Grafting*

    (i) Part of a stem or branch of one plant (the scion) is fitted into a notch cut in the root stock of another plant.

    (ii) The graft is bound together and after a few weeks, the scion and stock will have grown together to produce a single healthy plant.

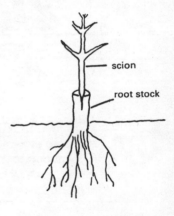

⇒ C5/62 + C6/62

57

Asexual reproduction in plants

G7 *[Describe asexual reproduction by runners and tubers.]*

Many plants can reproduce by the process of asexual reproduction. (Asexual = non-sexual, i.e. **not** involving gamete cells from two parents.)

1. *Runners* (e.g. strawberry)

    A parent plant sends out a horizontal shoot. Where this touches the soil a new plant will form. The parent provides food through the runner until the new plant can make its own, then the runner shrivels away.

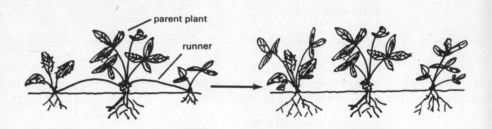

2. *Tubers* (e.g. potatoes)

    A potato plant sends out underground stems which swell up at the tip to form potatoes. The parent plant dies in the autumn. The following spring, each potato sends out shoots and roots, becoming a complete plant and starts the process again.

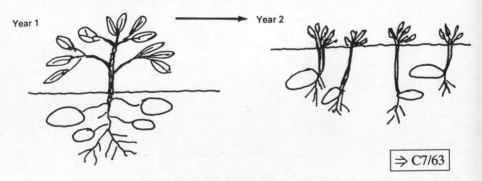

⇒ C7/63

CREDIT LEVEL

Temperature and germination

C1 *[Describe the changes in percentage germination that occur over a range of temperatures.]*

If the temperature is too low, the enzymes involved in bringing about germination will work slowly or not at all. If the temperature is too high, the enzymes may be destroyed.

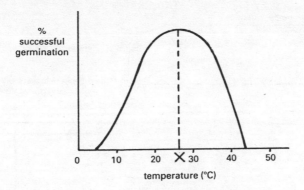

X = optimum (best) temperature for germination.

Each plant species has its own optimum germination temperature, depending on the climate that it is normally exposed to.

Insect and wind pollinated flowers compared

C2 *[Explain the structure of wind and insect pollinated flowers in relation to sexual reproduction.]*

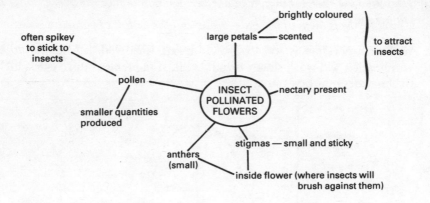

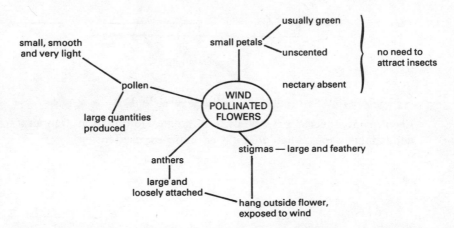

The differences in structure of insect and wind pollinated flowers are due to the following reasons:

Insect:

(a) The need to attract insects;

(b) the need to ensure that pollen is rubbed off anthers on to insects' bodies and on to stigmas of other flowers.

60

Wind:

(a) the need to produce large quantities of pollen;

(b) to increase the chances of catching pollen.

Growth of the Pollen Tube

[C3] *[Describe the growth of the pollen tube and the fusion of gametes.]*

Following pollination (the transfer of pollen from one flower to another by insects or wind), the male gamete inside the pollen grain has to travel to the ovary and fuse (join) with the female gamete.

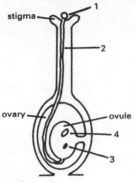

The pollen grain (1) grows a pollen tube (2) which grows down from the stigma towards the ovary. The tip of the tube enters the ovule and the male gamete (3), which has been carried along in the tube, enters the ovule and fuses with the female gamete (4). The joining of the two gametes is called **fertilisation**.

Seed dispersal

[C4] *[Describe one example of each of the following different seed dispersal mechanisms (wind, animal — internal, animal — external).]*

After fertilisation, the ovule develops into a seed containing an embryo plant.

Seeds must be dispersed (spread) away from the parent plant to avoid overcrowding and competition between parent and seedlings.

Three mechanisms of seed dispersal are described below.

Method	*Examples*	*Explanation*
1. Wind	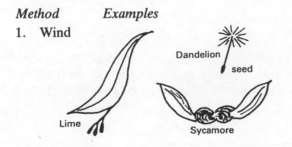	Light seeds with wing-like extensions or "parachutes" blown some distance from parent plant.

61

Method	*Examples*	*Explanation*
2. Animal (internal)	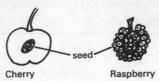	Seeds contained in a fruit (usually soft and juicy). Animals eat fruit, but seeds pass out undigested in droppings some distance from parent plant.
3. Animal (external)		Dry hooked fruits containing seeds catch on passing animals and drop off later, some distance from parent plant.

Advantages of artificial propagation

C5 *[Explain the advantages to humans of artificial propagation in flowering plants.]*

   (i) Identical offspring:
        All the desirable features of the parent plant are retained in the offspring (a clone).

   (ii) Speed:
        Many plants can quickly be produced from one parent, e.g. by taking cuttings.

   (iii) Grafting:
        The best features of two different plants can be combined in one.

Cloning plants

C6 *[State what is meant by the term "clone".]*

Artificial propagation can produce many new plants all from the same parent. As the new plants have grown from pieces of the parent plant, they will all be identical to the parent plant and to each other. The identical offspring of a single parent produced in this way are known as a **clone**.

Advantages and disadvantages of sexual and asexual reproduction in plants

C7 *[Explain the advantages and disadvantages of both sexual and asexual reproduction in plants.]*

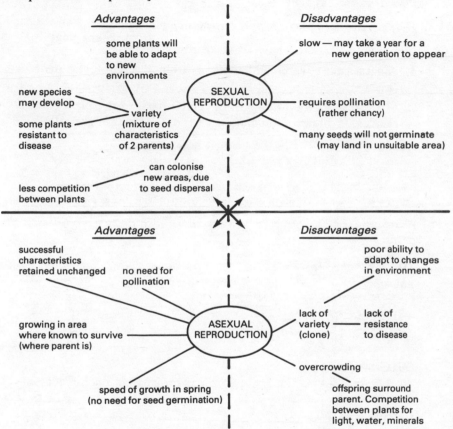

 Note how the advantages of one form of reproduction are linked to the disadvantages of the other form.

Some plants are capable of both forms of reproduction (e.g. strawberry fruits and runners) and therefore obtain the benefits of both.

63

SUB-TOPIC (c) — Making Food

GENERAL LEVEL

Plant transport system

G1 *[Explain the need for transport systems in a plant.]*

Unlike animals, plants have two transport systems:

1. To transport water and minerals from the soil to all parts of the plant.
2. To transport food made in the green parts of the plant (mainly the leaves) to all non-food making parts of the plant (e.g. roots).

Substance	Source	Destination	Main Purpose(s)
water	soil	all living cells	(i) raw material in making food (ii) keeping cells turgid
minerals	soil	all living cells	needed for correct plant growth
sugar	leaves	all non-green cells	(i) to provide energy for living cells (ii) for building new cells

G2 *[Describe the movement of water through xylem and food through phloem.]*

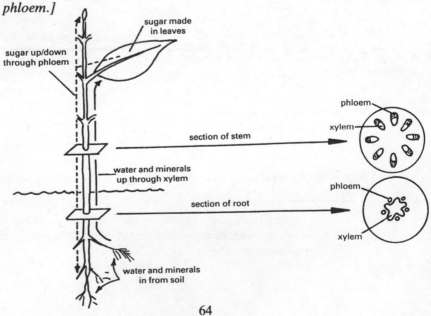

Xylem

Water is taken in through root hairs and transported up the stem through xylem vessels. These are hollow columns of dead cells and they form continuous tubes reaching all parts of the plant.

Phloem

Phloem tissue takes sugar solution from the leaves to non-food producing parts of the plant.

Vascular bundles

(a) Roots: Xylem tissue forms a star-shaped rod of cells running up the middle of the root. Smaller rods of phloem tissue lie between the arms of the star. (See diagram on page 64.)

(b) Stem: Vascular bundles lie around the outside of the stem. Each is a rod of phloem tissue to the outside and xylem tissue to the inside.

Veins

Veins are vascular bundles that leave the stem and go out into a leaf.

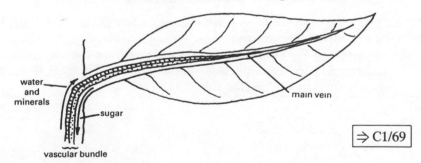

⇒ C1/69

Taking in carbon dioxide . . .

G3 *[State that plants take in carbon dioxide from the air through stomata which can open and close.]*

Fact: Carbon dioxide gas is needed by green plants as a raw material for making carbohydrate.

Fact: Carbon dioxide is present in air. (CO_2 makes up approximately 0·04% of atmospheric air.)

Problem: The outer surfaces of leaves are almost waterproof and gas proof. Carbon dioxide cannot easily get through them.

c

Solution: Leaves have many tiny holes called *stomata* (singular; stoma) which the plant can open and close. Carbon dioxide can enter the leaf through these stomata.

View of lower surface of a leaf

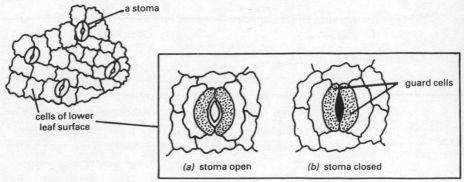

(a) stoma open   (b) stoma closed

. . . but losing water

G4 *[State that water vapour is lost through stomata.]*

When the stomata are open to allow carbon dioxide to enter the leaf, water vapour diffuses out in the other direction. Too much evaporation of water vapour from the leaves (called *transpiration*) may cause the cells to become flaccid and the plant wilts. When this happens, the guard cells close together, shutting the stomata and reducing water loss.

$$\Rightarrow C2/70$$

Making starch

G5 *[State that green plants make their own food which may be stored in the form of starch.]*

G6 *[State that green leaves convert light energy to chemical energy using chlorophyll.]*

Plants make their own food by the process called *photosynthesis*. (*Photo* = with light, *synthesis* = making.)

The end product of photosynthesis is sugar which may be converted to starch for storage. This can be shown by the following experiment:

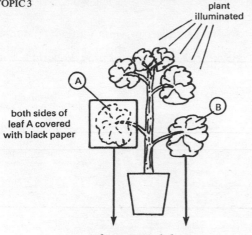

plant illuminated

A
both sides of leaf A covered with black paper

B

after several days leaves tested for starch

Result: Leaf A — starch absent
Leaf B — starch present

[Note: The plant should be "destarched" before starting, by being placed in the dark for several days, causing any starch in the leaves to be used up.]

Starch test for leaves

1. Leaf boiled in water to kill and soften leaf.
2. Leaf boiled in alcohol to remove green colour (chlorophyll) to make starch test easier to see.
3. Leaf softened again in water.
4. Leaf covered in iodine: black = starch present, brown = starch absent.

Conclusion: The plant has used light energy to make starch, i.e. it has converted light energy into chemical energy (in the starch).

That the green pigment chlorophyll is essential for photosynthesis can be shown by carrying out the starch test on a variegated leaf (one which is not all green).

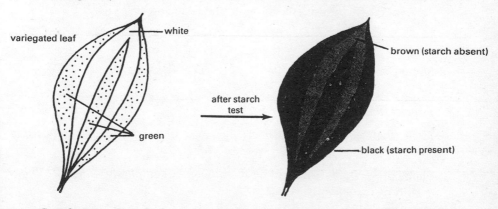

variegated leaf — white

green

after starch test

brown (starch absent)

black (starch present)

Conclusion: Starch is only produced in areas where chlorophyll is present.

⇒ C3/70

Summary of Photosynthesis

G7 *[Describe the process of photosynthesis in terms of raw materials and products.]*

Raw Materials	Energy source	Products
Carbon dioxide + water	sunlight	sugar + oxygen
	(chlorophyll also needed to absorb light, but is **not** used up)	(sugar stored as starch)

⇒ C4/71

CREDIT LEVEL

Structure of xylem and phloem

C1 *[Describe the structure of xylem and phloem and identify other functions of the transport system.]*

Xylem: vertical section

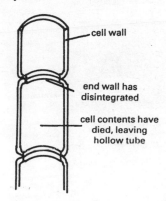

cell wall

end wall has
disintegrated

cell contents have
died, leaving
hollow tube

Part of a xylem vessel showing bands of *lignin*. This tough woody material strengthens the xylem.

As well as transporting water and minerals, xylem strengthens root and stems. Lignified xylem is what makes wood rigid.

Phloem:

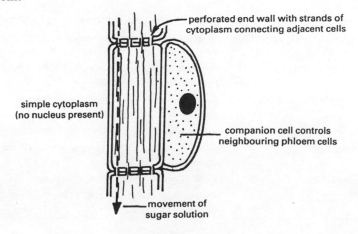

perforated end wall with strands of
cytoplasm connecting adjacent cells

simple cytoplasm
(no nucleus present)

companion cell controls
neighbouring phloem cells

movement of
sugar solution

Structure of a typical leaf

[C2] *[Describe the external features and internal structure (epidermis, mesophyll, veins) of a leaf in relation to its function in gas exchange.]*

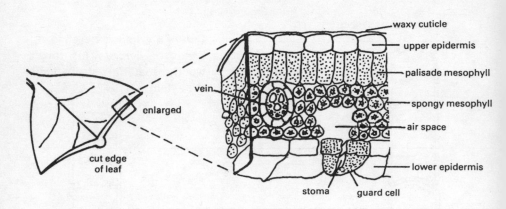

Structure	Function
Waxy cuticle	Reduces evaporation of water through epidermis.
Upper and lower epidermis	Protect more delicate cells inside from bright light, cold, drying out, etc.
Palisade mesophyll	Where most photosynthesis takes place. These cells contain many chloroplasts.
Spongy mesophyll	Some photosynthesis. Not as many chloroplasts as palisade cells.
Air spaces	Allow gases to move freely around inside the leaf.
Stoma	Allow gas exchange with atmosphere. (CO_2 in, O_2 and water vapour out.)
Guard cells	Control opening and closing of stomata.
Vein	Delivers water and minerals. Takes away sugars produced by mesophyll cells.

Carbohydrates in the plant

C3 *[Describe the fate of carbon dioxide as structural and storage carbohydrates in plants and as energy sources.]*

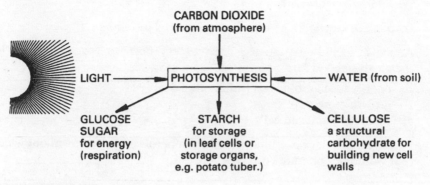

Limiting factors

C4 *[Explain what is meant by a limiting factor and describe the main limiting factors in the process of photosynthesis.]*

Carbon dioxide
Light   } Environmental factors all needed
Sufficient heat   for photosynthesis.

If any of these is lacking, photosynthesis will not take place as fast as it should, e.g.

1. *Frosty but sunny winter day*
   Temperature is too low for enzymes to work well, so **temperature** is the limiting factor.
2. *Cloudy but warm summer day*
   Light intensity is below optimum, so **light** is the limiting factor.
3. *Warm sunny summer day*
   Carbon dioxide is now likely to be the limiting factor.

TOPIC 4

ANIMAL SURVIVAL

SUB-TOPIC (a) — The Need for Food

GENERAL LEVEL

Why do we need to eat?

G1 *[Explain in simple terms why food is required by animals.]*

Animals, including humans, need to eat because food provides the chemicals needed for:

1. energy (see aerobic respiration page 48);
2. growth of new cells;
3. repair of damaged cells.

Food also provides essential **vitamins**, **minerals** and **water**, without which cells would not operate correctly.

$$\Rightarrow C1/76 + C2/76$$

The need for digestion

G2 *[State that digestion is the breakdown of large particles of food into smaller particles to allow absorption through the wall of the small intestine and into the blood stream.]*

1. The wall of the small intestine is made of cells.
2. Food must pass through these cells before it can enter the blood capillaries surrounding the intestine.
3. Only small molecules can pass through cell membranes. (See sub-topic 2(b) page 33.)
4. Most food is made up of very large molecules, e.g. starch, proteins, fats, etc.
5. Food must therefore be broken down (digested) into molecules small enough to pass through the gut wall.

$$\Rightarrow C3/76$$

The action of teeth

G3 *[Describe the role of different types of teeth in the mechanical breakdown of food in*

(a) a human (omnivore)
(b) a carnivore, e.g. dog
(c) a herbivore, e.g. sheep.]

(a) Human teeth

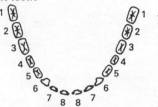

1, 2 and 3 = molars
4 and 5 = premolars
6 = canine
7 and 8 = incisors

Note: upper and lower jaw are identical in humans.

Tooth type	Shape	Function
Incisors	chisel shaped	cutting and biting food
Canines	sharp and pointed	biting and tearing food
Premolars	flattened, but with two cusps (raised parts)	tearing and grinding food
Molars	large and flattened, but with four or five cusps	chewing and grinding food

(b) Carnivore, e.g. dog

Tooth type	Shape	Function
Incisor	sharp, pointed	biting off small pieces of meat
Canines	large, sharp and pointed	gripping and killing prey
Premolars and Molars	scissor-like (the carnassial teeth) or flattened	slicing meat crushing bones

(c) Herbivore, e.g. sheep

Tooth type	Shape	Function
Incisors and Canines	small and chisel shaped	gripping and tearing grass
Premolars and Molars	larger, broad and with enamel ridges	grinding and chewing grass

The digestive system of mammals

G4 *[Identify the main parts of the mammalian alimentary canal and associated organs.]*

You should be able to name all of the following parts of the mammalian digestive system (alimentary canal).

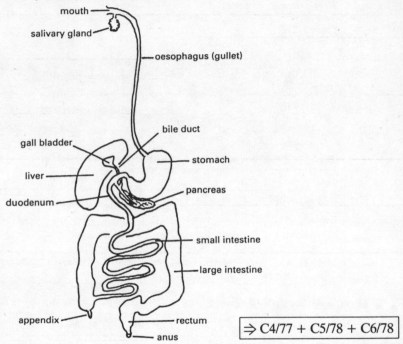

⇒ C4/77 + C5/78 + C6/78

Enzyme action

G5 *[State that different enzymes are responsible for the breakdown of carbohydrates, proteins and fats.]*

As food passes through the alimentary canal, enzymes are produced which break the food down into the smaller molecules of which it is made, e.g.

stomach lining produces protein-digesting enzymes, pancreas produces fat, protein and carbohydrate-digesting enzymes.

⇒ C7/78

Absorbing the products of digestion

G6 *[Explain how the structure of the small intestine is related to its function.]*

The **function** of the small intestine is to absorb the products of digestion, i.e. to take the small molecules resulting from the breakdown of the large food molecules, through the wall of the gut and into the bloodstream.

The **structure** of the small intestine is very efficient at doing this for the following reasons:

  (i) The small intestine is **very long**.

 (ii) The inner surface is folded into millions of finger-like *villi* (singular, villus).

These two features provide a **very large surface area** for absorption.

(iii) The lining of the villi is very thin, allowing digested food to pass quickly into the blood stream.

$\Rightarrow$ C8/79

The large intestine

G7 *[Describe the role of the large intestine in water absorption and elimination.]*

Undigested food, largely fibre, i.e. cellulose from plant material, passes into the large intestine along with a lot of water.

The main function of the large intestine is to absorb much of this water to prevent the body from drying out. Water passes through the walls of the large intestine into the bloodstream and the semi-solid waste that remains is stored in the rectum until it passes out through the anus. This is called *elimination* and the solid wastes are called *faeces*.

CREDIT LEVEL

The main food types

C1 *[State the chemical elements present in carbohydrates, proteins and fats.]*

C2 *[Describe the structure of carbohydrates, proteins and fats in terms of simple sugars, amino acids, fatty acids and glycerol.]*

Carbohydrates

Examples: sugars (e.g. glucose, sucrose) and starch.
Function: energy giving foods.
Chemical elements: carbon   hydrogen   oxygen
                        | | |
                   CARBO —   HYDR —   ATE   (ATE ending means "containing oxygen".)

Structure: All carbohydrates are made up of one or more simple sugars.
  glucose ■   single simple sugar molecules
  maltose ■—■   pairs of simple sugar molecules
  starch   ■—■—■—■—■—■—■ . . . long chains of simple sugars.

Proteins

Examples of protein-rich foods: lean meat, cheese, egg white, nuts.
Function: needed for growth and repair of cells.
Chemical elements: carbon, hydrogen, oxygen, nitrogen.
Structure: All proteins are made up of long chains of smaller molecules called *amino acids.*

Fats

Examples of fat-rich foods: milk products, margarine, animal fat, oily fish (e.g. herring).
Function: energy store, heat insulation.
Chemical elements: carbon, hydrogen, oxygen.
Structure: Fats are made up of two different types of smaller molecules.

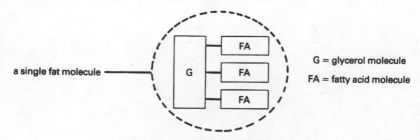

a single fat molecule ⟶

G = glycerol molecule
FA = fatty acid molecule

Insoluble → soluble food

C3 *[Explain that digestion involves the breakdown of insoluble food substances into soluble food substances.]*

Only liquids can pass through the gut wall, so food must be dissolved in water before it can pass through. Not only are large molecules like starch too big to pass through the membrane, they are also virtually insoluble.

Digestion makes them into smaller, soluble molecules so they may pass through the membranes of the gut lining.

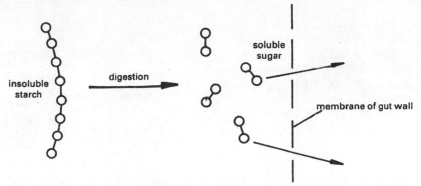

Production of digestive "juices"

C4 *[State the sites of production of the main digestive juices in a mammal.]*

Digestive Juice	Where Produced	Substrate	Product
Saliva	salivary glands in mouth and tongue	starch	maltose
Gastric juice	stomach lining	protein	peptides
Pancreatic juice	pancreas	proteins and peptides	amino acids
		starch	maltose
		fats	fatty acids and glycerol
Intestinal juice	lining of small intestine	peptides	amino acids
		fats	fatty acids and glycerol
		maltose	glucose
Bile	liver	Bile is **not** a digestive enzyme. It emulsifies fat, i.e. it breaks large lumps of fat into many small lumps, to increase the surface area to speed up enzyme reaction.	

Swallowing . . . and further

C5 *[Explain the mechanism of peristalsis.]*

Food is pushed through the digestive system by muscles surrounding the gut. Waves of muscular contraction called *peristalsis* run from top to bottom of the alimentary canal, keeping the food moving.

Section through intestine

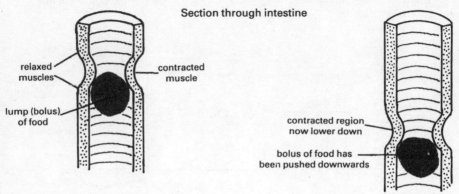

C6 *[Explain how the contractions of the stomach help in the chemical breakdown of food.]*

Muscles in the stomach wall churn the food and digestive juices together. This mixing helps the digestive juices to begin the chemical breakdown of food (particularly protein).

Some digestive enzymes

C7 *[Give an example of an amylase, a protease and a lipase. State their substrates and products.]*

Name of Enzyme	Where Produced	Substrate	Product
Salivary amylase	salivary glands	starch	maltose
Pepsin (a protease or protein digesting enzyme)	stomach lining	protein	peptides
Pancreatic lipase	pancreas	fats	fatty acids and glycerol

Absorption of food in the small intestine

C8 *[Explain how the structure of a villus including the lacteal and the blood capillaries are related to the absorption and transport of food.]*

The surface area of the small intestine is greatly increased by millions of tiny hair-like structures called *villi*. This increased surface area is necessary for efficient absorption of digested food.

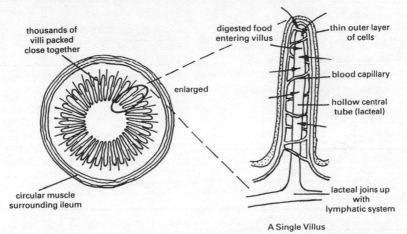

A Single Villus

Glucose (digested carbohydrate)
Amino acids (digested protein) } pass through outer layer of cells and into blood capillaries which carry them away to the rest of the body.

Fatty acids and glycerol (digested fat) enter central lacteal. From there, they are transported by the lymphatic system, eventually being emptied into the bloodstream elsewhere in the body.

SUB-TOPIC (b) — Reproduction

GENERAL LEVEL

Eggs and Sperm

G1 *[Describe the main features of sperm and eggs.]*

Eggs	Sperm
Produced by females	Produced by males
Smaller numbers produced	Very large numbers produced
Much larger than sperm	Much smaller than eggs
Are not "self propelled"	Have "tails", so can swim
Contain food reserves	Have very limited food reserves.

Typical Egg Cell   Typical Sperm Cell

External or Internal Fertilisation

G2 *[State that in some fish, sperm are deposited in water close to the eggs and that in mammals, sperm are deposited in the body of the female.]*

G3 *[Describe the process of fertilisation.]*

Sexual reproduction involves the joining together (fusion) of a reproductive cell (a gamete) from a male, with another from a female.

Males produce sperm cells and females produce egg cells (sometimes called ova).

Gametes, like other cells, have nuclei containing genetic material that carry some of the characteristics of the parent. When sperm and egg fuse together, the nuclei join and this genetic information 'mixes' together.

This process is called *fertilisation* and leads to a new individual having a mixture of characteristics from both parents.

How do sperm and eggs meet?

In many animals, including most fish, the female lays her eggs into the water and the male releases his sperm near the eggs. The sperm then swim through the water to reach the eggs. This is *external fertilisation* as it takes place **outside** the animal's body.

In other animals, in particular all mammals, the female retains the egg in her body and the male deposits sperm directly into the female's body. *Internal fertilisation* then takes place **inside** the female's body.

$\Rightarrow$ C1/84

Production of eggs and sperm

G4 *[State that sperm are produced in testes.]*

G5 *[State that eggs are produced in ovaries and are released into oviducts, where, in mammals, fertilisation takes place.]*

In all male animals, sperm are made in *testes*.
In all female animals, eggs are made in *ovaries*.

Fertilisation in mammals

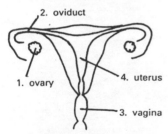

2. oviduct
1. ovary
4. uterus
3. vagina

Female Reproductive Organs
(front view)

1. *Ovary* releases eggs.

2. Egg passes down *oviduct*.

3. If copulation takes place, male's penis releases sperm into *vagina*.

4. Sperm swim up through the *uterus* and if they meet the egg coming down the oviduct, one sperm will fuse with the egg and fertilisation will take place.

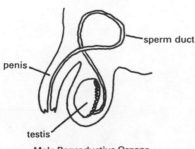

sperm duct
penis
testis

Male Reproductive Organs
(side view)

81

Development in fish

G6 *[State that in fish, eggs are protected by flexible coverings and that the embryos obtain food from the enclosed yolk.]*

G7 *[State that in a fish, like the trout, the young emerge from the eggs able to maintain themselves.]*

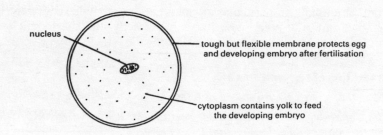

nucleus

tough but flexible membrane protects egg and developing embryo after fertilisation

cytoplasm contains yolk to feed the developing embryo

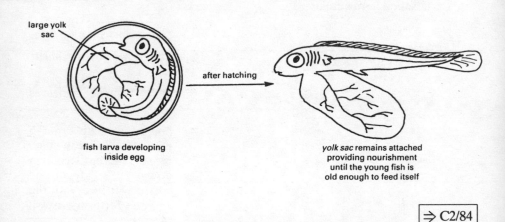

large yolk sac

after hatching

fish larva developing inside egg

yolk sac remains attached providing nourishment until the young fish is old enough to feed itself

⇒ C2/84

Development of mammals

G8 *[Describe how the fertilised egg passes down the oviduct and becomes attached to the wall of the uterus, develops in fluid of the amniotic sac and obtains food from the maternal circulation.]*

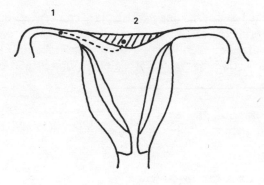

1. After fertilisation in the oviduct, the egg divides rapidly.

2. When it arrives in the uterus, it is a ball of cells and it sinks into the wall of the uterus. From now on it receives food and oxygen from the mother's blood as it continues to develop.

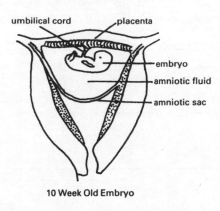

10 Week Old Embryo

The embryo's blood is pumped through the umbilical cord to the placenta where it picks up food and oxygen.

The embryo is bathed and protected by amniotic fluid contained in the amniotic sac.

⇒ C3/85

Care after birth

G9 *[State that at birth, the young of mammals are dependant on the adult for care and protection.]*

Unlike fish, mammals depend on their parents for some time after birth. As well as feeding the young mammals on milk produced by the mother, the parents protect the young from danger and cold.

CREDIT LEVEL

Fertilisation in land-living animals

C1 *[Explain the importance of internal fertilisation to land-living animals.]*

Land-living animals do not have water into which they can release eggs and sperm. The eggs, therefore, are retained inside the female's body and during the act of copulation, sperm are passed by the male into the female's body. Once inside, they **are** in a watery environment and can swim towards the egg.

Internal fertilisation is one of the evolutionary developments that allowed reptiles, birds and mammals to become true land-living animals.

Improving the chances of successful reproduction

C2 *[Explain the relationship between the number of eggs/young produced and the amount of protection given during fertilisation and development in fish and mammals.]*

	Number of eggs laid	Chances of fertilisation	Protection of eggs	Parental protection of young	Chances of successful development
Fish	large number	low	none (or very little)	none (or very little)	poor
Mammals	few	high	protected inside mother's body	young are dependant on parents for food and protection	high

Structure and function of the placenta

C3 *[Describe the structure and function of the placenta.]*

Functions of the placenta

To allow exchange of substances between the mother's and the embryo's blood.

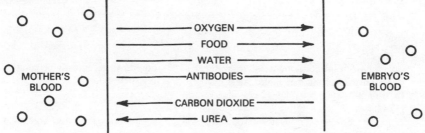

These exchanges all take place without the mother's and embryo's blood coming in contact. This is important, as they may have different blood types.

Structure of the placenta

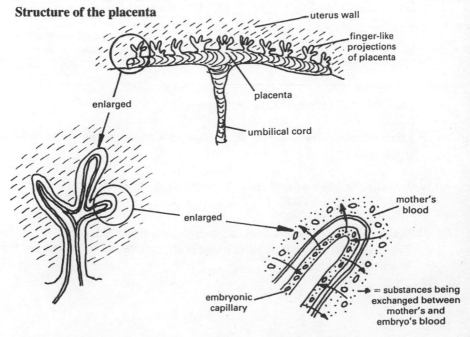

SUB-TOPIC (c) — Water and Waste

GENERAL LEVEL

Water gain and loss in animals

G1 *[Identify the ways in which a mammal gains and loses water.]*

Water Gain	Water Loss
Food most food contains a lot of water, especially fruit, vegetables, meat, etc.	*Urine* liquid waste, mostly a solution of *urea* in water.
Drink all drinks are water-based: tea, coffee, milk, etc.	*Faeces* semi-solid waste, also contain a lot of water.
Body chemistry chemical reactions in the body make a small amount of water.	*Sweat* more lost in hot weather, but we lose some water through sweating even in cold weather.
	Breath exhaled air comes from the lungs saturated with water vapour.

Structure and function of the kidneys

G2 *[State that the kidneys are the main organs for regulating the water content in a mammal.]*

G3 *[Identify the position and state the functions of the kidney, renal arteries and veins, ureter and bladder.]*

Water intake will sometimes be more, sometimes less, than water loss. Regulating the amount of water in the body, so that the balance is just right, is done by the kidneys.

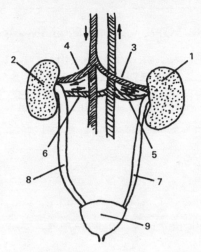

Name	Function
1. left kidney 2. right kidney }	Filter blood. Remove excess water and urea.
3. 4. } renal arteries	Supply blood to the kidneys
5. 6. } renal veins	Take filtered blood away from the kidneys and back into the general circulation.
7. 8. } ureters	Take urine (urea and water) from the kidneys to the bladder.
9. bladder	Stores urine until it can be passed out of the body.

⇒ C1/89

How the kidneys work

G4 *[State that the kidneys work by filtration of blood and reabsorption of useful materials such as glucose.]*

G5 *[State that urea is a waste product removed in the urine.]*

Filtration

As blood flows through the kidneys, a lot of the water and most of the substances dissolved in the plasma are filtered out. This includes urea, glucose, amino acids and salt.

Reabsorption

Many of these substances are needed by the body, so they are then taken back into the blood. This is called reabsorption. **Urea** (a waste product) and just the right amount of **water** that the body needs to lose are **not** reabsorbed and so pass out of the kidneys, down to the bladder and out of the body as urine.

$\Rightarrow$ C2/90 + C3/91

Kidney disease

G6 *[Explain the implications of damage to the kidneys by accidents or disease.]*

If both the kidneys stop working through disease or accident, the body will be unable to

1. Remove poisonous urea from the blood.
2. Regulate the amount of water in the body. Excess water will build up in the body.

Through a combination of these two, total kidney failure quickly causes death, unless treated.

$\Rightarrow$ C4/91

CREDIT LEVEL

Regulation of water balance

C1 *[Explain the role of ADH in the regulation of water balance.]*

The amount of anti-diuretic hormone (ADH) secreted by the brain depends on the concentration of the blood.

If the blood is **too watery**, e.g. after drinking a lot, ADH production is **reduced** and the kidneys produce **lots of dilute urine**.

If the blood is **too concentrated**, e.g. when dehydrated or after eating a lot of salt, ADH production is **increased** and the kidneys produce **a small amount of concentrated urine**.

Summary

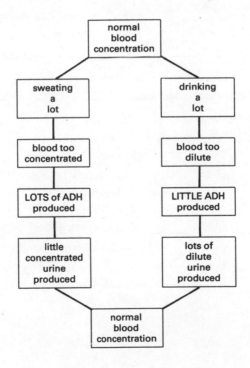

Urine production in the kidneys

C2 *[Explain the process of urine production using a simple diagram of the nephron.]*

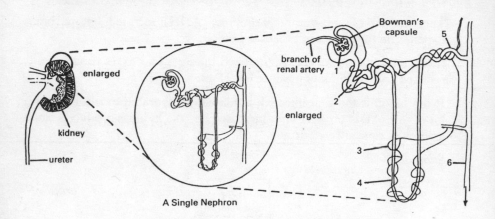

A Single Nephron

Each kidney has approximately one million nephrons.

Part of Nephron	Function
1. capillaries (Glomerulus)	Blood is filtered and collects in the capsule.
2. kidney tubule	Useful substances reabsorbed, e.g. glucose, amino acids, and pass back
3. capillaries	into capillaries (3).
4. Loop of Henle	Some salt reabsorbed.
5. tubule	More salt reabsorbed.
6. collecting duct	Final reabsorption of water. The amount reabsorbed here is controlled by ADH.

The source of urea

C3 *[State the source of urea in the body and describe how urea is transported to the kidneys.]*

Urea is formed in the *liver* from the breakdown of surplus amino acids.

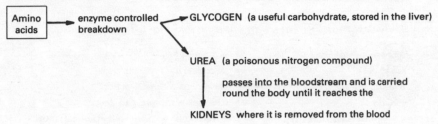

When kidneys stop working

C4 *[Describe the benefits and limitations of replacement and "artificial" kidneys.]*

If kidneys are damaged or diseased, they may stop working and then the body is unable to get rid of excess water and poisonous urea. Kidney failure can be treated by:

1. *Kidney transplant* — a donor kidney from another person is placed inside the patient's body and connected to an artery and to the bladder.

2. *Kidney machines* (artificial kidneys) — several times a week the patient's blood is passed through a machine which removes urea and excess water.

Each method has benefits and limitations.

Benefits	Limitations

Transplant
  Patient can live an almost normal life
  (e.g. can go on holiday).
  Not dependant on a machine.
  Patients can eat and drink normally.
	Tissue rejection may cause new kidneys
	to fail.
	Patient on drugs for rest of life
	Drugs may make patient more likely
	to catch infectious diseases.
	Not enough suitable kidneys available.

Kidney Machine
  No drugs necessary.
  Availability of machines only
  limited by money.
	Patient's diet very restricted.
	Patient must always be near a machine.
	Machines may break down.

SUB-TOPIC (d) — Responding to the Environment

GENERAL LEVEL

Environmental factors that affect behaviour

G1 *[Give examples of environmental factors that affect behaviour.]*

Environmental Factor	Example of Effect
Light/dark	nocturnal hunters, e.g. owls.
Moisture/dryness	frogs remain close to water.
Heat/cold	cats seek warm place to sleep.
Chemicals (including pH)	Paramecium (a single-celled animal) moves towards weak acid.
Oxygen concentration	fish avoid water low in oxygen.
Day length	nesting behaviour of birds in spring.

⇒ C1/94

Animal responses to changes in environmental factors

G2 *[Describe the response of an animal to change in one environmental factor.]*

The response of woodlice to light and dark can be shown using a choice chamber.

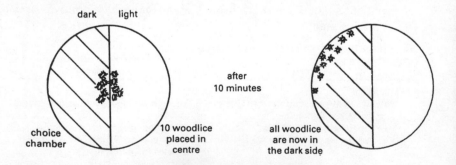

(*Note:* Woodlice do **not** move deliberately towards the dark area. They move at random within the choice chamber and when they enter the dark area, they slow down and eventually stop.)

Rhythmical behaviour in animals

G3 *[Describe examples of rhythmical behaviour and in each case identify the external trigger stimulus.]*

Examples of rhythmical behaviour	*Trigger stimulus*
Bird migration	Changes in day length.
Hibernation of bears	Change in environmental temperature.
Cockroaches more active at night	On-set of darkness.
Mating of Grunion (a fish)	High tide (caused by position of moon).

Note: The **trigger stimulus** is the particular environmental factor which causes the behaviour to start.

⇒ C2/94

CREDIT LEVEL

The importance of responding to environmental stimuli

C1 *[Explain the significance of responding to environmental stimuli.]*

Some examples from G1:

		Importance
1.	Frogs remain in damp areas.	They need water for external fertilisation. Also, they need moist skin to assist in gas exchange.
2.	Fish avoid water low in oxygen.	If they swim into water with little oxygen, they may suffocate.
3.	Birds begin nesting in response to longer day length in spring.	Young will have a plentiful supply of food in warmer weather of late spring / early summer.

The importance of rhythmical behaviour in animals

C2 *[Explain the significance of rhythmical behaviour in named animals.]*

Some examples from G3:

		Importance
1.	Geese migrate from Arctic Circle to Europe in autumn (and back again in spring).	Avoid severe weather of Arctic winter. More food available in Europe.
2.	Grunion gather for mating at a particularly high tide.	Ensures fertilisation of eggs by bringing males and females together.
3.	Cockroaches become more active at night.	They avoid predators by feeding at night.

SUB-TOPIC (a) — Movement

GENERAL LEVEL

The Skeleton — Support, Movement and Protection

G1 *[State that the skeleton provides a framework for support and muscle attachment.]*

G2 *[State that the skeleton protects the heart, lungs, brain and spinal cord.]*

The skeleton has three main functions

1. *Support* — to hold us up against the force of gravity.
2. *A means of movement* — the skeleton provides a rigid framework for the attachment of muscles.
3. *Protection* — All of the vital organs upon which the body depends for survival are protected by the skeleton.

Vital Organ	Protected by
brain	skull
spinal cord	vertebrae of the backbone
heart	rib cage
lungs	rib cage

Joints

G3 *[Describe the range of movements allowed by a ball and socket joint and by a hinge joint.]*

Joints between neighbouring bones allow movement, but at the same time are strong enough to provide support. Most joints have a limited amount of movement.

Type of Joint	Examples	Movement allowed
Ball and socket	Hip, shoulder	All directions
Hinge	Knee, elbow	One direction only

Ligaments and Cartilage

G4 *[State the functions of ligaments and cartilage at a joint.]*

In a joint, neighbouring bones must be allowed enough movement for the joint to work properly. They must not be allowed to move too much, however, or the joint would become dislocated. This could result in damage to the joint.

Ligaments are tough fibrous tissues which hold bones together at a joint and prevent dislocation.

As a joint moves, neighbouring bones rub against one another. To reduce friction, the ends of the bones are covered with **cartilage** which is very smooth and slippery.

Cartilage is also rubbery, so it acts as a shock absorber when the bones are forced together.

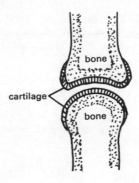

$\Rightarrow$ C1/98

The Structure of Bone

G5 *[State that bone is composed of flexible fibres and hard minerals.]*

Healthy bones are hard and slightly bendy. The hardness provides good support while the slight flexibility reduces breaks by allowing bones to bend slightly under stress.

The flexibility is provided by many **flexible fibres** running throughout the bone.

Hardness is provided by minerals containing calcium and phosphate.

$\Rightarrow$ C2/98

Tendons

G6 *[State that muscles are attached to bones by tendons.]*

G7 *[Describe how movement is brought about by muscle contraction.]*

When a muscle contracts, it becomes **shorter** and fatter. One end is usually attached to a rigid part of the skeleton and the other to a moveable part of the skeleton.

For example, raising the forearm.

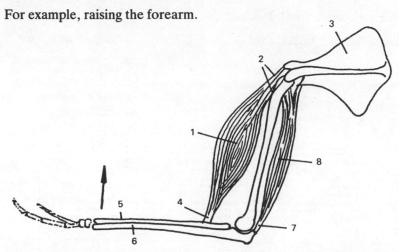

The *biceps* muscle (1) contracts. *Tendons* (2) pull on the *shoulder blade* (3) which cannot move, being attached to the rest of the skeleton. Lower tendon (4) pulls on the *radius* (5) which is raised. The *ulna* (6) is also raised and this pulls tendon (7) which stretches the *triceps* muscle (8).

$$\Rightarrow \text{C3/99} + \text{C4/99}$$

D

CREDIT LEVEL

Synovial Joints

C1 *[Describe the structure of a synovial joint and state the functions of its parts.]*

A synovial joint is a joint lubricated by synovial fluid which is secreted by the synovial membrane surrounding the joint. The hip, shoulder, elbow, knee and finger are all synovial joints.

Structure of a synovial joint

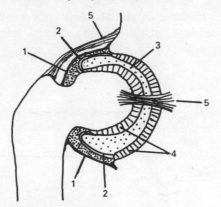

Function of Parts

1. *Capsule* surrounds and protects the joint.

2. *Synovial membrane* secretes synovial fluid.

3. *Synovial fluid* sticky liquid that lubricates the joint.

4. *Cartilage* smooth rubbery substance covering ends of bones to cushion joint.

5. *Ligament* holds the two bones together.

Structure of Bone

C2 *[State that bone is formed by living cells.]*

Magnified section through bone

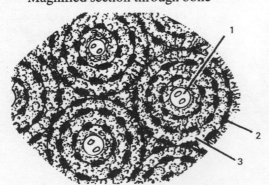

1. Canal containing blood vessels.

2. Living cells which secrete calcium salts.

3. Hard bone made of calcium salts (mostly calcium phosphate).

Properties of Tendons

C3 *[Explain why tendons are inelastic.]*

Tendons connect muscles to bones. When a muscle contracts, the tendon pulls on the bone and causes movement. Because tendons are tough and inelastic (not stretchy) movements can be very fast and precise. Any stretchiness in tendons would make accurate movement very difficult.

Opposing Muscles

C4 *[Explain the need for a pair of opposing muscles at a joint.]*

Muscles can contract and make themselves shorter, but they cannot stretch themselves back to their original length. This can only happen if they are **pulled** back to their original length by another muscle pulling in the opposite direction.

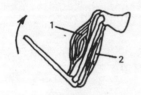

1. The *biceps* has contracted and raised the forearm.

2. The *triceps* has been stretched to full length.

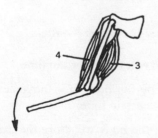

3. The *triceps* can now contract to straighten the forearm.

4. The *biceps* has now been stretched to its full length, ready to contract once more.

Pairs of **opposing** muscles, like these two, are found at all moveable joints.

SUB-TOPIC (b) — The Need for Energy

GENERAL LEVEL

The Need for Energy

Muscular contraction causing body movement is one of the main uses of energy in the body.

There is a constant need for energy, as muscles are working all the time, awake or asleep, e.g. heart muscle.

The energy for this activity comes from food, in particular carbohydrates such as sugar and starch (see Topic 2, sub-topic (e) and Topic 4, sub-topic (a)).

The amount of energy needed depends on age, sex and occupation.

Generally

> Children still growing need more energy than old people.
> Males need more energy than females.
> Those with strenuous occupations, e.g. labourer, need more energy than those with less strenuous jobs, e.g. office worker.

The Effect of Energy Imbalance

G1 *[State the effects of the imbalance between energy input and output.]*

> *Energy input* = total energy of all food eaten in a certain time.

> *Energy output* = total energy used up by the body (for movement, making heat, etc.) in a certain time.

If energy input is **more than** energy output, the body will store the extra energy in the form of fat, and the body will **gain weight**.

If energy input is **less than** energy output, the body will take the extra energy it needs from stored body fat and the body will **lose weight**.

Exchange of Gases

G2 *[State that oxygen is absorbed and carbon dioxide released in breathing.]*

Oxygen for aerobic respiration is obtained from the atmosphere when we take air into our lungs. Carbon dioxide produced as a waste product by aerobic respiration passes out of our body when we breathe out.

	Composition of Air	
	inhaled (%)	exhaled (%)
Oxygen	21	17
Carbon dioxide	0·03	4
Nitrogen	79	79

Structure of the Lungs

G3 *[Describe the structure of the lungs.]*

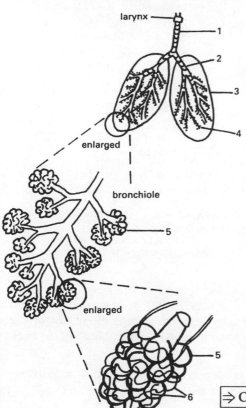

Air passes from the mouth and nose down the *trachea* (1). This divides to form two *bronchi* (singular — bronchus (2)), one going to each *lung* (3).

Each bronchus divides many times into smaller *bronchioles* (4) which take air deep into the lung.

Each bronchiole ends in a number of thin-walled air sacs (5).

The air sacs are covered with a network of *blood capillaries* (6).

$\Rightarrow$ C1/105 + C2/105 + C3/106 + C4/106

101

Structure and Function of the Heart

G4 *[Identify the four chambers of the heart.]*

G5 *[Describe the path of blood flow through the heart and blood vessels connected to it.]*

G6 *[Describe the positions and functions of the heart valves.]*

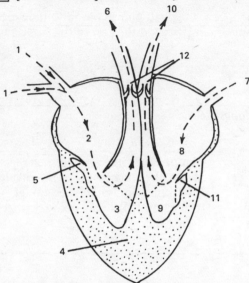

The four chambers of the heart are:

Right atrium   (2)
Right ventricle (3)
Left atrium   (8)
Left ventricle (9)

(*Note:* left and right are reversed in a diagram of the heart.)

Blood takes the following path as it passes through the heart:

Blood returns from the head, arms and rest of the body through a large vein, the *vena cava* (1).

Blood enters the *right atrium* (2). When it is full, the muscular wall squeezes blood into the *right ventricle* (3).

When the ventricle is full the thick muscular wall (4) contracts. The heart valve (5) closes and stops blood going back to the atrium.

Blood leaves the heart through the *pulmonary artery* (6) and goes to the lungs.

After passing through the lungs, blood returns to the heart through the *pulmonary vein* (7) and enters the *left atrium* (8). It squeezes blood into the *left ventricle* (9). When full, the ventricle pumps blood out of the heart through the *aorta* (10). Another valve (11) stops blood going back into the left atrium.

The pulmonary artery and aorta also have valves (12) to stop blood flowing back into the heart between beats.

The Heart — a Living Pump

G7 *[Explain the difference in thickness of the walls of the ventricles.]*

G8 *[State that the heart obtains its blood supply from coronary arteries.]*

G9 *[State that blood leaves the heart in arteries, flows through capillaries and returns to the heart in veins.]*

The heart is really two pumps in one. One half pumps blood to the lungs and back, the other half pumps blood all round the rest of the body and back.

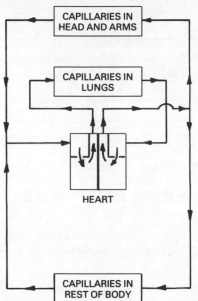

Note: Blood leaves the heart through *arteries*, passes through *capillaries* in the organs of the body, then returns to the heart through *veins*.

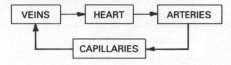

The heart is a muscular bag and needs a good supply of oxygen and food. This is provided by the *coronary arteries* which branch off from the aorta.

What Causes the Pulse

G10 *[State that the pulse indicates that blood is flowing through an artery.]*

Each time the heart beats (about 70 times a minute on average), blood is pushed into the arteries under high pressure. This causes the walls of the arteries to bulge as the blood flows through them. Each heartbeat can be felt as a pulse in the arteries.

Blood

G11 *[Describe the function of red blood cells and plasma in the transport of respiratory gases and food.]*

Blood consists of *red cells* and *white cells* carried in a liquid called *plasma*.

Red Cells

top view   section

Size — tiny (about 5·5 million per cubic millimetre).
Filled with red pigment *haemoglobin*.
Function — to **transport oxygen** from the lungs to the tissues.
Unusual in having **no nucleus**.

Plasma

Yellowish coloured liquid.
Functions — **to transport cells**
          — **to carry dissolved food** (in particular glucose and amino acids) from intestines to rest of body.
          — **to carry dissolved carbon dioxide** from tissues to lungs for removal from body.

[Extra: Blood also transports white blood cells which fight disease, hormones, salts, urea, blood clotting factors and distributes heat around the body.]

⇒ C5/107

Gas Exchange between Blood and Cells

G12 *[Describe gas exchange between the body cells and the surrounding capillaries.]*

Blood entering capillaries in the tissues is saturated with oxygen. The cells near the capillaries are low in oxygen because they use it up as soon as they get it. This causes a *concentration gradient* between blood and cells, so oxygen rapidly diffuses from the blood into the cells.

⇒ C6/107

CREDIT LEVEL

Mechanism of Breathing

C1 *[Describe the mechanism of breathing in humans.]*

Air is forced in and out of the lungs by contraction of the *intercostal muscles* and the *diaphragm muscles*.

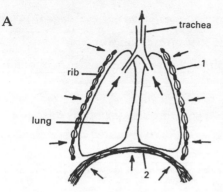

In diagram A the intercostal muscles (1) and the diaphragm (2) are relaxed and in this position have squeezed air out of the lungs.

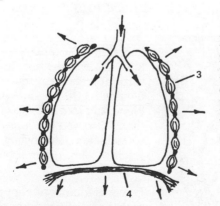

In diagram B the intercostal muscles have contracted (3), lifting the rib-cage upwards and outwards. The diaphragm muscles have pulled the diaphragm downwards (4). These two movements expand the lungs and draw in air.

Trapping Dust and Germs

C2 *Explain the function of mucus, cilia and cartilage in the trachea and bronchi.]*

Dust and germs breathed in are trapped in sticky *mucus* produced by cells in the lining of the trachea and bronchi.

105

Tiny hairs called *cilia* in the lining of the trachea and bronchi push the mucus with trapped dirt up to the larynx from where it passes down the oesophagus into the stomach. Acid in the stomach kills the germs.

The trachea and bronchi are strengthened by bands of *cartilage* which stop the air passages from collapsing during breathing.

Efficient Gas Exchange

C3 *[Describe the features which make lungs efficient gas exchange structures.]*

Lungs are efficient gas exchange structures because:

1. *Surface area* for gas exchange is very large (due to millions of air sacs).

2. The gas exchange surface (walls of air sacs) is *very thin*, allowing oxygen and carbon dioxide to pass through quickly by diffusion.

3. The gas exchange surface is *moist* so oxygen and carbon dioxide can dissolve so that diffusion can take place.

4. Millions of capillaries provide a good *blood supply* to the air sacs.

Gas Exchange in the Air Sacs

C4 *[Describe gas exchange between the air sacs and the surrounding blood vessels.]*

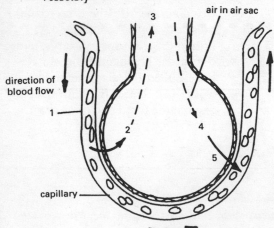

air in air sac

direction of blood flow

capillary

Blood in the capillary at (1) is low in oxygen but high in carbon dioxide, so carbon dioxide diffuses out of the blood and into the air sac (2), then passes up the bronchioles, bronchus and trachea as we breathe out (3).

Oxygen follows the opposite path and diffuses from the air sac (4) into the capillary (5).

The Function of Haemoglobin

C5 *[Explain the function of haemoglobin in the transport of oxygen.]*

Haemoglobin is the red pigment in red blood cells responsible for transporting oxygen from the lungs to the tissues.

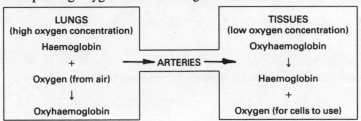

Efficient Gas Exchange between Blood and Cells

C6 *[Describe the features of a capillary network which allow efficient gas exchange.]*

A *large surface area* due to arteries dividing many times into *tiny capillaries* and the *thin walls* (one cell thick) of capillaries make them very efficient at exchanging oxygen and carbon dioxide between the blood and tissues.

SUB-TOPIC (c) — Co-ordination

GENERAL LEVEL

Two Eyes are Better than One

G1 *[State that judgement of distance is more accurate using two eyes rather than one.]*

Any activity that requires judgement of distance, e.g. catching a ball, driving, etc., is more accurate with two eyes than one.

⇒ C1/111

Structure and Function of the Eye

G2 *[Identify the cornea, iris, lens, retina, optic nerve and state their functions.]*

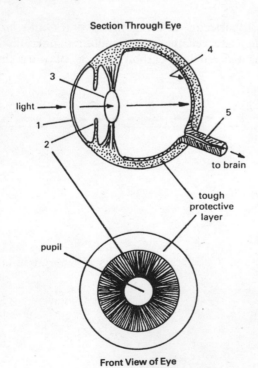

Section Through Eye

Front View of Eye

Light enters the eye through the transparent *cornea* (1). The amount of light entering the eye is controlled by the *iris* (2). Light passes through the hole in the middle of the iris (the pupil) and is focussed by the *lens* (3). Light forms an image on a thin layer of light-sensitive cells at the back of the eye, the *retina* (4). Nerve impulses from these cells pass along the *optic nerve* (5) to the brain which interprets them as sight. The eye is protected by a tough white outer layer which we see as the 'white' of the eye.

Hearing

G3 *[State that judgement of direction of sound is more acurate using two ears rather than one.]*

With sight, distance judgement is better with two eyes, and with hearing, judgement of **direction** of sound is better with two ears that it would be with only one.

Structure and Function of the Ear

G4 *[Identify the ear drum, middle ear bones, cochlea, auditory nerve and semi-circular canals and state their functions.]*

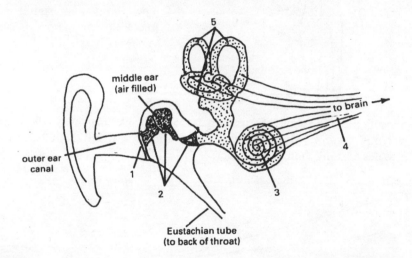

Sound waves pass down the outer ear canal and hit the *ear drum* (1), causing it to vibrate. The vibrations are carried by the tiny *middle ear bones* (2) to the fluid filled inner ear.

Nerves in the coiled *cochlea* (3) detect the vibrations in the fluid and send impulses along the *auditory nerve* (4) to the brain where they are interpreted as sounds.

The three semi-circular canals (5) detect movement not sound. When the head moves, nerve impulses are sent to the brain giving information about movement which helps us balance

⇒ C2/111

The Nervous System

G5 *[State that the nervous system is composed of the brain, spinal cord and nerves.]*

G6 *[State that nerves carry information from the senses to the central nervous system and from the central nervous system to the muscles.]*

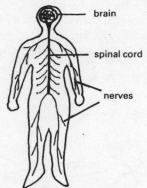

brain

spinal cord

nerves

The human nervous system.

The brain and spinal cord make up the *central nervous system* (CNS).

Sensory nerves relay information from the sense organs to the central nervous system. Motor nerves carry impulses from the CNS to the muscles causing them to contract.

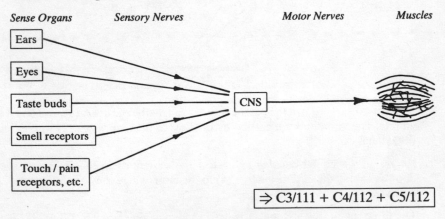

⇒ C3/111 + C4/112 + C5/112

110

CREDIT LEVEL

Binocular Vision

C1 *[Explain the relationship between judgement of distance and binocular vision.]*

Each eye forms a slightly different image due to the eyes being several centimetres apart. The brain receives these two images and combines them into one. From the difference between the two images of an object, the brain is able to estimate how far away the object is. If the object is moving towards or away from us, binocular vision helps to estimate speed of movement.

Semi-circular Canals Again

C2 *[Explain how the arrangement of semi-circular canals is related to their function.]*

The three semi-circular canals are at right angles to each other, so whichever direction the head moves, at least one is stimulated. The three directions detected are:
1. up and down (nodding head),
2. rotating (shaking head),
3. side to side (ear down towards shoulder).

The Reflex Arc

C3 *[Describe how a reflex action works, using a simple drawing of a reflex arc.]*

Reflex actions are fast movements usually to prevent damage occurring to the body. Nerve impulses travel from a sense organ to the spinal cord which causes a very fast muscle contraction.

Example: Jerking hand away from a hot object.

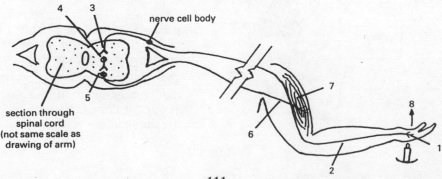

Pain receptors in the back of the hand are stimulated (1). A nerve impulse travels up a *sensory neurone* (2). The impulse crosses a *synapse* (junction) (3) to an *intermediate neurone* (4) inside the spinal cord. The impulse crosses another synapse (5) and travels down a *motor neurone* (6). The motor neurone stimulates a muscle in the arm to contract (7) which jerks the hand away from the flame (8). As the brain is not involved, this all happens very fast, reducing the damage done to the hand.

Responding to Stimuli

C4 *[State that the CNS sorts out information from the senses and sends messages to those muscles which make the appropriate response.]*

The CNS receives information all the time (even when asleep) about our surroundings and about our internal environment. A lot of this information needs no action to be taken and is 'filtered out' before it reaches the conscious part of our brain, e.g. background noises that you only notice when they stop.

Some information must be acted upon very fast before the body is damaged, e.g. jerking hand away from a hot object. This is called a *reflex action* and does not involve the brain.

Other information will be analysed by the brain before any action is taken.

The Brain

C5 *[Identify the cerebrum, cerebellum and medulla and state their function.]*

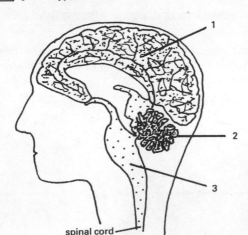

spinal cord

The *cerebrum* (1) is the part of the brain responsible for

* thought
* memory
* interpreting information from the sense organs
* movement of the body.

The *cerebellum* (2) is responsible for balance and fine control of muscles, making our movements precise and coordinated.

The *medulla* (3) looks after the automatic functions such as controlling heart beat, breathing, etc.

SUB-TOPIC (d) — Changing Levels of Performance

GENERAL LEVEL

Muscle Fatigue

G1 *[State that continuous or rapidly repeated contraction of muscle results in fatigue.]*

G2 *[State that muscle fatigue results from a lack of oxygen and a build up of lactic acid.]*

If a muscle stays contracted for a long time, or contracts and relaxes rapidly for a long time, it begins to suffer from muscle fatigue (muscle tiredness).

Examples:

1. Continuous contraction: Carrying a heavy shopping bag, your hands and arms get tired.

2. Rapidly repeated contraction: In a running race, your arms and leg muscles get tired.

Muscles need *food* and *oxygen* to work properly. In the examples above, these may not be supplied by the blood fast enough (particularly oxygen). If muscles contract when they are not getting enough oxygen, they work very inefficiently and *lactic acid* builds up in the muscle tissue. It is this substance that causes muscle fatigue.

$\Rightarrow$ C1/116

113

The Effect of Exercise on Pulse Rate and Breathing Rate

G3 *[Explain why pulse rate and breathing rate increase with exercise.]*

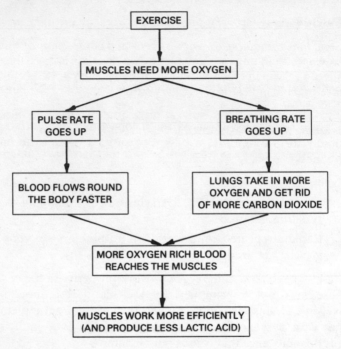

The Effect of Training

G4 *[State that with exercise, the pulse rate, breathing rate and lactic acid level rise less in an athlete than in an untrained person.]*

An athlete is "fitter" than an untrained person because heart rate and breathing rate rise less in an athlete and an athlete's muscles also produce less lactic acid.

Recovery Time

G5 *[State that recovery time is the time taken to return to normal levels of pulse rate, breathing rate and lactic acid.]*

G6 *[Describe how recovery time can be used as an indication of physical fitness.]*

Pulse and breathing rate and lactic acid level are not reliable indicators of fitness as there is much variation of these even between unfit people. A more reliable indicator is *recovery time*.

Recovery time is the time it takes, after exercise, for pulse rate, breathing rate and lactic acid level to return to normal.

A fit person's recovery time will be shorter than that of an unfit person.

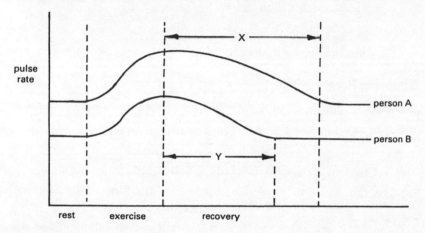

Notice that:

1. Person A has a higher resting pulse rate (unreliable indicator).
2. A's pulse rate rises more than B's during the period of exercise.
3. A's recovery time (X) is longer than B's (Y).

This indicates that B is fitter than A.

Note:

1. Recovery time can also apply to breathing rate and lactic acid level.
2. This comparison can only be made if the two people are similar in size, age, sex and do identical exercises for the same time.

⇒ C2/116 + C3/116

115

CREDIT LEVEL

Anaerobic Respiration in Muscles

C1 *[Explain muscle fatigue in terms of anaerobic respiration.]*

In aerobic respiration (Topic 2(e)) energy is released from food with the help of oxygen. When muscles cannot get enough oxygen for aerobic respiration, they can use **anaerobic respiration** to release a little energy from food.

Disadvantages of anaerobic respiration:

1. It is much **less efficient** than aerobic respiration (less energy is released from food).

2. It produces **lactic acid** which causes muscle fatigue.

Advantage of anaerobic respiration:

It is able to keep cells alive for a short time in the absence of oxygen.

Improving Recovery Time

C2 *[State that training improves the efficiency of the lungs and circulation.]*

C3 *[Explain the relationship between the effects of training and recovery time.]*

Training improves the efficiency of the body in the following ways:

1. The lungs absorb oxygen and pass it to the blood faster (removing carbon dioxide from the blood faster also).

2. The heart increases in size and strength and so pumps blood round the body faster.

These two effects mean that after exercise, oxygen can be quickly supplied to muscles to break down the lactic acid that has built up during anaerobic conditions. This is called *paying back the "oxygen debt"*. The faster this is done, the shorter is the recovery time.

SUB-TOPIC (a) — Variation

GENERAL LEVEL

What is a "Species"?

G1   *[State that a species is a group of interbreeding organisms whose offspring are fertile.]*

Similar animals (or plants) may breed with each other. If they produce offspring that are fertile, i.e. can also reproduce, they are said to belong to the same *species*.

Organisms that cannot breed with each other, or do breed, but produce infertile offspring, e.g. horse × donkey → mule (sterile offspring), are said to be members of *different species*.

Variation within Species

G2   *[State that variation can occur within a species.]*

Although members of a species show many similarities (characteristics of the species), individuals will show many differences, e.g. tough spiky leaves are characteristics of holly, but the number of spikes and colour of the leaf may vary.

Types of Variation

G3   *[Give examples of continuous and discontinuous variation.]*

Continuous variation:

A feature of an animal or plant such as length or weight, that can be anywhere in a range from the smallest to the largest.

Examples: 1. height of sweet pea plants;
               2. weights of people in a slimming club;
               3. heights of people on a bus;
               4. length of mouse tails.

Discontinuous variation:

A feature of an animal or plant that falls into two or more distinct groups.

Examples: 1. flower colour of sweet peas;
2. attached or unattached ear lobes in humans;
3. human blood groups (A, B, AB or O);
4. smooth or wrinkled maize kernels.

$\Rightarrow$ C1/119

CREDIT LEVEL

Continuous or Discontinuous?

C1 *[Explain what is meant by continuous and discontinuous variation.]*

Continuous variation

Example: Height of sweet pea plants.

In a group of sweet pea plants, one will be the smallest and one will be the tallest. In between, the other plants will form a **continuous range of sizes**.

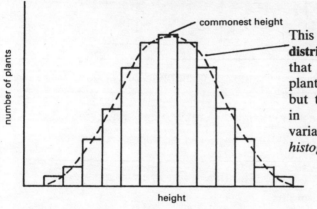

commonest height

This is called a **normal distribution curve**. It shows that there are a few small plants, and a few tall plants, but the commonest height is in between. Continuous variation is often shown by a *histogram*.

Discontinuous variation

Every member of the population must belong to one or other of the possible groups.

Example: Flower colour of sweet peas.

Discontinuous variation is shown by a *bar graph*.

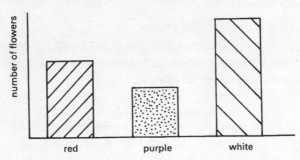

When trying to decide if an example is continuous or discontinuous, ask yourself these two questions:

1. Can I separate the example into a number of separate categories?

    Answer — Yes — discontinuous
             No — continuous.

2. Would the example best be shown as a histogram or a bar graph?

    histogram — continuous
    bar graph — discontinuous.

120

SUB-TOPIC (b) — What is Inheritance?

Inherited Characteristics

G1 *[State that certain characteristics are determined by genetic information received from the parents and give examples from animals and plants.]*

Each of us has characteristics that can be seen in our parents and grandparents. This is also true of other animals and plants. This is because 'information' which determines these characteristics is passed on from parents to offspring. The nature of this genetic information is explained later in this sub-topic.

Examples of inherited characteristics.

(a) Humans: tongue rolling, red hair, shape of nose, etc.

(b) Animals: fur colour, eye colour in fruit flies, etc.

(c) Plants: leaf shape, flower colour in peas, tallness/dwarfness in peas, etc.

Different Phenotypes

G2 *[Identify examples of phenotypes of the same characteristic.]*

Most physical characteristics can appear in a number of different forms. These different forms are called *phenotypes*.

Examples.

		Characteristic	*Different phenotypes*
(a)	Humans	hair colour	fair, dark, red
		hair type	straight, wavy, curly
(b)	Animals	wing shape in fruit flies	straight, curved
		fur colour in mice	black, white, grey, etc.
(c)	Plants	height of pea plants	tall, dwarf
		colour of maize kernels	yellow, white, purple.

"True-Breeding" Characteristics

G3 *[Identify examples of true-breeding, dominant and recessive characteristics from the numbers and phenotypes of given crosses.]*

G4 *[Identify generations as P, F1 and F2 from given examples of crosses.]*

Pollen from the flowers of a tall pea plant is used to pollinate flowers on another tall pea plant. The seeds are later collected and planted to produce the next generation. This can be shown as follows:

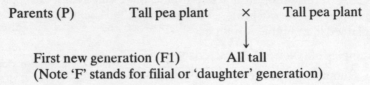

Parents (P)   Tall pea plant   ×   Tall pea plant

First new generation (F1)   All tall
(Note 'F' stands for filial or 'daughter' generation)

If two of these F1 plants are crossed:

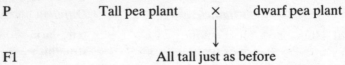

Tall pea plant   ×   Tall pea plant

Second new generation (F1)   Again all tall

When a characteristic is passed on unchanged like this generation after generation, the plants (or animals) are said to be *true-breeding* for that characteristic.

But if a tall pea plant is crossed with a **dwarf** pea plant:

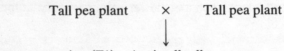

P   Tall pea plant   ×   dwarf pea plant

F1   All tall just as before

This shows that when the two phenotypes are 'mixed' in the F1 generation, only the **tall** phenotype seems to operate. This is called the *dominant* character. Dwarf does not appear when mixed with tall and so is called the *recessive* character.

If two of the F1 plants are now crossed:

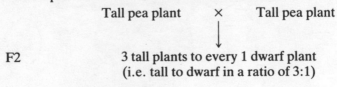

Tall pea plant   ×   Tall pea plant

F2   3 tall plants to every 1 dwarf plant
                      (i.e. tall to dwarf in a ratio of 3:1)

122

Note. Pea plants will probably produce more than 4 offspring, but however many they produce there should be roughly 3 times more tall plants than dwarf.

This shows that the **recessive phenotype** can appear again in the F2 generation.

$$\Rightarrow C1/129 + C2/129 + C3/129$$

Summary — so far

G5 *[State that the phenotypes of the F1 in a true-breeding cross are uniform.]*

In a **true-breeding** cross, all the offspring in the F1 **and** F2 generations will be the same as the parents.

In a **non true-breeding** cross, all the F1 offspring will show the **dominant phenotype**, but in the F2 generation there will be a **3:1 ratio** of dominant to recessive.

Chromosome Number

G6 *[State that each body cell has two matching sets of chromosomes.]*

The nucleus of a human body cell has 46 chromosomes. This is made up of two matching sets of 23 chromosomes. Other organisms (plants and animals) have different numbers, but they always consist of two matching sets.

G7 *[State that sex cells are called gametes.]*

G8 *[State that the reduction of the number of chromosomes to a single set occurs during gamete formation.]*

G9 *[State that each sex cell carries one set of chromosomes.]*

The sex cells, or *gametes* involved in sexual reproduction are formed by a special kind of cell division. This separates the two sets of chromosomes so that **one** complete set goes into each gamete.

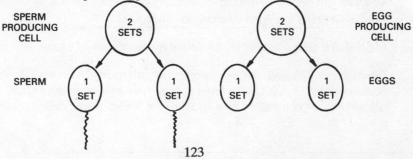

Sites of gamete production

	Animals	*Plants*
Male gametes	sperm in testes	pollen grains in anthers
Female gametes	eggs (ova) in ovaries	ovules in ovaries

Completing the Double Set Again

G10 *[Describe how a complete double set of chromosomes is achieved at fertilisation.]*

Fertilisation occurs when a male gamete joins with a female gamete. Each has a single set of chromosomes, so the fertilised egg cell then has two sets once again, **one set from each parent**.

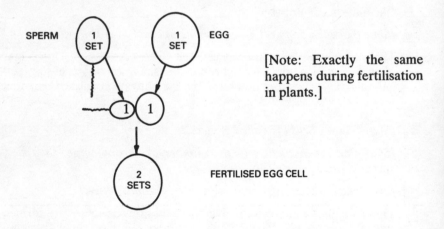

[Note: Exactly the same happens during fertilisation in plants.]

The Role of Genes

G11 *[State that genes are parts of chromosomes.]*

G12 *[State that a characteristic is controlled by two forms of a gene.]*

Information passed from parent to offspring is carried on the chromosomes. Each characteristic, e.g. hair colour, wing shape, flower colour, etc., is controlled by a section of a chromosome called a *gene*.

124

A pea plant may have white flowers or red flowers. This is because the gene for flower colour is in two forms; one for red, one for white. Most other characteristics in plants and animals are also controlled by two forms of a gene.

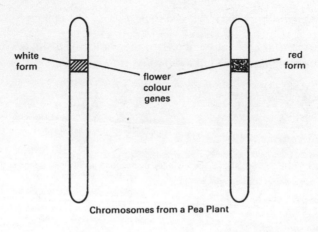

white
form

flower
colour
genes

red
form

Chromosomes from a Pea Plant

⇒ C4/130

125

The Monohybrid Cross

G13 *[State that each parent contributes one of the two forms.]*

G14 *[State that each gamete carries one of the two forms of the gene.]*

G15 *[State the meaning of the word genotype.]*

An experimental cross in which the inheritance of a **single** characteristic is being investigated is called a *monohybrid cross*, e.g.

P   MALE FRUIT FLY WITH LONG WINGS   FEMALE FRUIT FLY WITH VESTIGIAL WINGS

Both flies are TRUE BREEDING, i.e. long winged fly has 2 genes for long wings and vestigial winged fly has 2 genes for vestigial wings.

Each gamete carries ONE of these genes:

EVERY SPERM CELL CONTAINS *ONE* LONG WING GENE   EVERY EGG CELL CONTAINS *ONE* VESTIGIAL WING GENE

FERTILISATION

FERTILISED EGG CELL CONTAINS ONE LONG AND ONE VESTIGIAL WING GENE

F1   ALL F1 FLIES ARE LONG WINGED BECAUSE LONG IS *DOMINANT* AND VESTIGIAL IS *RECESSIVE*

126

If we now cross two of the F1 flies:

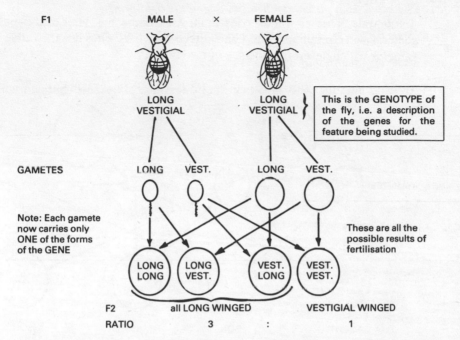

F1   MALE   ×   FEMALE

LONG   LONG   This is the GENOTYPE of
VESTIGIAL   VESTIGIAL } the fly, i.e. a description
                                                of the genes for the
                                                feature being studied.

GAMETES   LONG   VEST.   LONG   VEST.

Note: Each gamete   These are all the
now carries only   possible results of
ONE of the forms   fertilisation
of the GENE

            LONG   LONG   VEST.   VEST.
            LONG   VEST.   LONG   VEST.

F2   all LONG WINGED   VESTIGIAL WINGED
RATIO   3   :   1

In each generation, an individual will inherit one form of every gene
from its "father" and the other from its "mother".

$\Rightarrow$ C5/130

Determination of Sex

G16 *[State that the sex of a child is determined by specific chromosomes called X and Y chromosomes.]*

G17 *[State that in humans, each male gamete may have an X or a Y chromosome, while each female gamete has an X chromosome.]*

One of the 23 pairs of human chromosomes determines the sex of a person. A female has two identical chromosomes, called the X chromosomes, i.e. the female genotype is XX.

A male has two different chromosomes. One an X, the other a Y. (Male genotype is XY.)

G18 *[Explain how the sex of a child is determined with reference to the X and Y chromosomes.]*

The female gametes will all contain an X chromosome. Half of the male gametes will contain an X and half will contain a Y. Thus it is the **father's** gametes which determine the sex of the children.

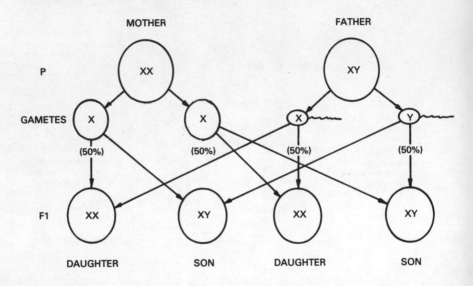

CREDIT LEVEL

More Monohybrid Crosses

C1 *[State that the parents in experimental monohybrid crosses are usually true-breeding and show different phenotypes of the same characteristic.]*

C2 *[Predict the proportions of the phenotypes of the F2 offspring of a monohybrid cross.]*

C3 *[Explain monohybrid crosses in terms of genotypes.]*

The original parents in a monohybrid cross are usually true-breeding. One with the dominant phenotype is crossed with one with the recessive phenotype.

From a given cross, you should be able to work out the genotype of parents (P), gametes, F1 offspring and by crossing two of the F1, the genotypes, phenotypes and ratios of the F2 offspring, e.g.

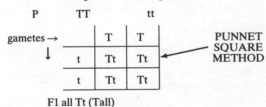

(Note: Capital letters are used to indicate the dominant form, e.g. T. Small t is used for the recessive in this case.)

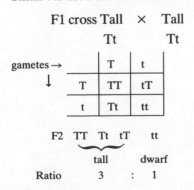

E

Alleles

C4 *[State that different forms of a gene are called alleles.]*

Whenever a gene exists in more than one form, these different forms are called *alleles*, e.g. **long** and **short** are two alleles of the fruit fly gene for wing length.

Other examples: *Characteristic*   *Alleles*
                  pea flower colour   red, white
                  pea height   tall, dwarf
                  human colour vision   normal, colourblind.

Differences Between Observed and Predicted Figures

C5 *[Explain differences between observed and predicted figures in monohybrid crosses.]*

The F2 generation of the pea cross above (in C3) **predicts** a ratio of tall to dwarf of 3:1.

In an **actual** cross with many plants, the results were 265 tall plants and 82 dwarf plants. This is a ratio of 3·2:1.

Actual ratios may differ from predicted ones for the following reasons:

1. The random nature of fertilisation.
2. Failure of seeds to germinate (in plants).
3. Death of seedlings/embryos.

SUB-TOPIC (c) — Genetics and Society

Selective Breeding

G1 *[Give two examples of an improved characteristic resulting from selective breeding.]*

The ancestors of modern crop plants and animals (such as wheat and beef cattle) were much poorer in the quality and quantity of their produce. Over hundreds of generations farmers have selected, for breeding purposes, the plants and animals that were the best of their generation. In this way, the genes for **desirable** characteristics, such as high yielding wheat, were passed on and **undesirable** genes were lost.

Other examples of characteristics improved by selective breeding:
1. Increased disease resistance in crop plants such as wheat;
2. Increased milk yield in dairy cattle;
3. Increased meat production in beef cattle;
4. Leaner meat, i.e. less fat, produced by beef cattle.

⇒ C1/133

Chromosome Mutation in Humans

G2 *[Describe an example of a human condition caused by a chromosome mutation, e.g. Down's Syndrome.]*

Down's Syndrome is one example of a human condition caused by a mistake made during production of gametes. One pair of chromosomes fails to separate so that one gamete has one extra chromosome. If this is passed on to the fertilised egg, the extra chromosome causes the symptoms associated with Down's Syndrome.

⇒ C2/134 + C3/134

Amniocentesis

G3 *[State that amniocentesis can be used to detect chromosome characteristics before birth.]*

If it is thought that a human embryo may have a genetic problem, such as Down's Syndrome, the chromosome characteristics of the embryo can be checked well before birth.

An *amniocentesis* is carried out by taking a sample of the amniotic fluid surrounding the embryo and looking at the embryo's cells that are in the fluid. The nucleus of a cell is photographed through a microscope and the chromosomes can be checked. If a serious abnormality is found, the mother may decide to have an abortion.

CREDIT LEVEL

Enhancing Characteristics by Selective Breeding

C1 *[Describe two examples, one plant, one animal, of the enhancement of a characteristic through selective breeding.]*

Plants

Four popular vegetables, cabbage, cauliflower, broccoli and brussels sprouts, have all been produced by selective breeding from a common ancestor. This has taken many generations.

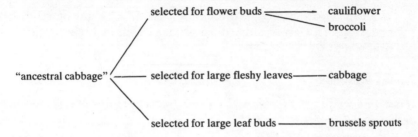

Animals

Different varieties of cattle have been produced through hundreds of years of selective breeding.

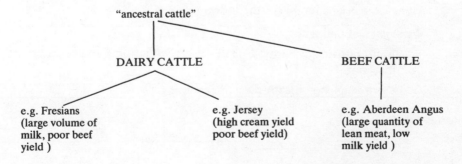

Advantageous Mutation

C2 *[Give an example of a chromosome mutation, advantageous to humans, in a plant or animal of economic importance.]*

Most mutations are harmful and the individual may not survive. Sometimes mutations can be beneficial and so the new characteristic is passed on to future generations.

Scientists are always on the lookout for plants and animals that, by mutation, have developed new and useful characteristics.

Examples of mutations that have economic importance.

1. A bacterium that can digest oil can help to clear up oil spills.
2. Modern bread wheat has multiple sets of chromosomes due to mutation. This gives it many advantages such as higher yield, over wild wheat.

Rate of Mutation

C3 *[Give an example of a factor which can influence the rate of mutation in an organism.]*

Chromosomes may mutate spontaneously, i.e. without any external cause. Most mutations, however, are due to some environmental factor. Such a factor is called a *mutagen* and it may work by changing the structure of a chromosome, or by damaging the mechanism which separates the sets of chromosomes during gamete formation. Down's Syndrome is an example of the latter.

Examples of mutagens.

1. Radiation, e.g. X-rays, ultra-violet, radiation from a radioactive material.
2. Chemicals, e.g. mustard gas, benzene.

TOPIC 7   BIOTECHNOLOGY

SUB-TOPIC (a) — Living Factories

GENERAL LEVEL

Biotechnology is — using living organisms to *(a)* produce a product for human consumption or *(b)* carry out a process, of benefit to humans.

This sub-topic deals mostly with **fermentation** by **yeast** — a form of biotechnology that has been known for thousands of years.

"Traditional" Biotechnology

G1 *[State that the raising of dough and the manufacture of beer and wine depend on the activities of yeast.]*

G2 *[Identify yeast as a single-celled fungus, which can use sugar as food.]*

Yeast is a single celled fungus used in bread making and also in making beer, wine and other alcoholic drinks.

Yeast uses **sugar** for food and it produces **carbon dioxide** gas (which makes dough rise) and **alcohol** as waste products.

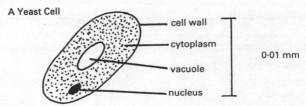

A Yeast Cell

cell wall

cytoplasm

vacuole

nucleus

0·01 mm

Fermentation by Yeast

G3 *[Using a word equation, state the process of fermentation of glucose by yeast.]*

Alcoholic fermentation is the name given to the process in which yeast uses sugar and produces carbon dioxide and alcohol.

Glucose (sugar) $\xrightarrow{\text{yeast enzymes}}$ carbon dioxide + ethanol (alcohol) + (heat) energy

$$\Rightarrow C1/137 + C2/137 + C3/138 + C4/139$$

Cheese and Yoghurt

G4 *[State that the manufacture of cheese and yoghurt depends on the activities of bacteria.]*

Another traditional type of biotechnology is the use of bacteria in making cheese and yoghurt.

Cheese

In cheese making, bacteria are used for:

(a) producing a chemical to clot milk,
(b) ripening the cheese,
(c) flavouring the cheese.

Blue cheeses, e.g. Stilton, have fungi added to them to produce the blue veins and characteristic flavour.

Yoghurt

Bacteria are used to:

(a) clot or thicken the milk,
(b) produce lactic acid which gives the 'sharp' flavour of yoghurt.

G5 *[State that the souring of milk is a fermentation process.]*

The production of lactic acid by milk bacteria is another type of fermentation.

⇒ C5/139

CREDIT LEVEL

Anaerobic Respiration

C1 *[Describe the process of anaerobic respiration and compare it with aerobic respiration.]*

Respiration (see Topic 2(e)) is the release of energy from food and takes place in every living cell. Most cells use oxygen to make this energy release efficient. This is *aerobic respiration*.

Some cells, however, can respire without oxygen. This is called **anaerobic** *respiration* (*an* = non) and it is **less efficient** as it releases less energy from the food than aerobic respiration.

Fermentation by yeast is an example of anaerobic respiration.

Word equations

1. *Aerobic Respiration*

   Glucose + oxygen ⟶ carbon dioxide + water + energy.

2. *Anaerobic Respiration*

   Glucose ⟶ carbon dioxide + ethanol + energy.

One proof that anaerobic respiration is less efficient than aerobic respiration is that ethanol produced in anaerobic respiration still contains a lot of useful energy, whereas water produced in aerobic respiration contains none.

Commercial Brewing

C2 *[Describe how commercial brewers provide the best conditions for yeast.]*

For efficient brewing, the best conditions for yeast must be provided. These are:
1. plenty of food,
2. the correct temperature,
3. sterile conditions.

1. **Food**

   This is sugar, usually in the form of **maltose** produced by germinating barley.

137

2. **Temperature**

    Ale yeasts work best at between 12 – 18 °C. Lager yeasts work best at between 8 – 12 °C. The fermentation process gives off heat, so the brewer must cool the fermentation vessel to the correct temperature.

3. **Sterile conditions**

    Any wild yeast or bacteria getting into the brew would spoil it, so all parts of the brewing process must be kept sterile, usually by steam cleaning before the brew is started.

Batch Processing

C3 *[Explain what is meant by the term "batch processing".]*

Traditional biotechnology such as brewing uses batch processing in which all the raw materials are put into the fermentation vessel and later the product is removed.

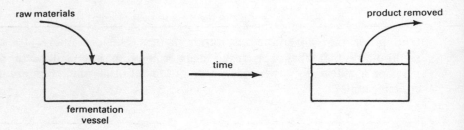

One disadvantage of this system is that the equipment must be thoroughly cleaned out between batches. This is time in which no product is being made and so no money is being earned.

Malting Barley

C4 *[Explain the need for malting of barley before use by the brewing industry.]*

Barley is used as the source of food for alcoholic fermentation by yeast in the brewing industry (and as the first stage of whisky making). The carbohydrate in barley is in the form of starch which must be converted to sugar before yeast can use it. This is done by germinating the barley.

Enzymes in the barley grains convert the starch to maltose (or "malt") during germination. In the brewing industry this process is called *malting* the barley.

Lactic Fermentation

C5 *[Explain the souring of milk in terms of bacterial fermentation of lactose.]*

A form of anaerobic fermentation by milk bacteria turns lactose (milk sugar) into lactic acid. This gives sour milk its acid taste and causes coagulation of the milk proteins.

lactose ⟶ lactic acid

SUB-TOPIC (b) — Problems and Profit with Waste

The Environmental Effect of Sewage

G1 *[Describe some examples of the damage done to the environment by disposal of untreated sewage.]*

G2 *[Give some examples of diseases which may be spread by untreated sewage.]*

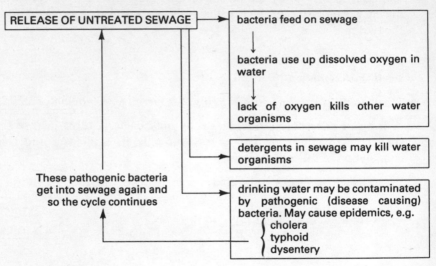

Handling Micro-organisms in the Laboratory

G3 *[Describe the precautions that must be taken during laboratory work with micro-organisms.]*

G4 *[Explain the importance of such precautions in any biotechnological work.]*

Precautions	*Reasons for precautions*
1. Hands washed before and after work.	Remove bacteria picked up from environment / remove any picked up during lab work.
2. Benches swabbed with disinfectant.	Remove bacteria and spores from bench.
3. Lab coat should be worn.	Protect clothes from bacteria.
4. Use only safe bacterial cultures provided.	Other sources, e.g. air, soil, etc., may contain pathogenic bacteria.
5. Autoclave all equipment and growth media.	Heat in autoclave kills all foreign bacteria.
6. Work beside bunsen, flaming loops and necks of culture bottles.	Prevent entry of foreign bacteria and kill cultured bacteria on loops, etc.
7. Incubate bacterial cultures below body temperature.	This discourages the growth of pathogens which grow best at 37 °C.
8. Autoclave all equipment after use and cultures before disposal.	Kill all bacteria in case any pathogens have appeared.

$$\Rightarrow C1/146 + C2/146 + C3/148$$

Sewage Treatment — Bacterial Decay in Action

G5 *[State that sewage treatment involves its breakdown by decay micro-organisms to products harmless to the environment.]*

One of the main dangers of releasing untreated sewage is that it provides ideal food for bacterial growth. This may then harm the environment. (See G1 and G2.)

If this bacterial growth is contained within a sewage treatment plant, the environmental damage is avoided.

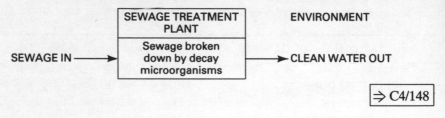

⇒ C4/148

G6 *[Describe how the oxygen required by micro-organisms can be provided during sewage treatment.]*

"Sewage-eating" bacteria need oxygen. This can be provided in three ways.

1. Trickling the sewage through **filter beds**. Air spaces between the stones provide oxygen.

2. Bubbling **compressed air** through tanks containing **activated sludge** (sewage with added sewage-eating bacteria).

3. **Agitation** of activated sludge. Stirring mixes in oxygen from the air.

⇒ C5/148

Making Use of Waste

G7 *[Give two examples of **useful** products made from waste by micro-organisms. Explain the economic importance of this technology.]*

Industry can **save** money by using micro-organisms to clean up waste that would otherwise need expensive treatment.

Industry can make money by selling the products made by some of these micro-organisms.

Examples:

1. **Animal food** can be made from yeast grown on waste sugar solution.
2. Protein-rich **animal food** can be made by bacteria fed on methanol from the petrochemical industry.
3. **Biogas** (methane) can be made by decay bacteria in domestic waste dumps.
4. **Biogas** can also be made by bacteria breaking down animal dung.

$\Rightarrow$ C6/149

Fuel from Micro-organisms

G8 *[State that alcohol and methane are products of fermentation.)*

G9 *[Explain the advantages of fermented fuel compared to fossil fuel.]*

A fuel is something that can be burned to release energy. Alcohol and methane are two fuels produced by a fermentation process carried out by micro-organisms in the absence of oxygen.

Alcohol — by fermentation of sugar by yeast.
Methane — by fermentation of waste by bacteria.

Fermented fuel has several advantages over fossil fuel (coal, oil and gas):

1. Fermented fuel is a **renewable supply** whereas fossil fuels are **non-renewable**, i.e. one day they will run out.
2. Using fermented fuel for energy preserves oil, etc., for use as raw materials in the chemical industry.
3. Fermented fuel is 'cleaner'. It releases less environmentally harmful chemicals when burnt than fossil fuels.

143

The Growth and Harvesting of Micro-organisms

G10 *[State that under suitable conditions, micro-organisms can reproduce very rapidly by asexual means.]*

G11 *[State that micro-organisms may be harvested to provide protein-rich food for animals or humans.]*

Given suitable conditions (warmth, food, moisture and oxygen) micro-organisms can reproduce very rapidly. This is an example of **asexual reproduction;**

e.g. bacteria.

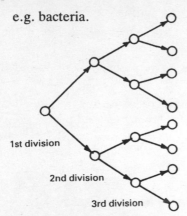

1st division

2nd division

3rd division

In this way, a single bacterium can produce over 1 million bacteria after only 20 divisions. Under ideal conditions, bacteria can reproduce approximately every 20 to 30 minutes. At this rate, 1 million bacteria can be produced in under 10 hours.

Such rapid growth on relatively cheap and simple food makes micro-organisms very suitable for the production of protein-rich foods for animals and humans.

Examples:

1. Yeast for cattle food (and 'Marmite').
2. 'Pruteen', a single-celled fungus for cattle food.
3. 'Quorn', a mycoprotein fungus for human consumption.

CREDIT LEVEL

Handling Micro-organisms in Industry

C1 *[Explain the precautions taken during manufacturing processes with reference to resistant fungal and bacterial spores.]*

In most industrial processes involving micro-organisms, the greatest danger is of foreign bacteria or fungi getting into the process rather than the cultured micro-organisms escaping.

Some bacteria and fungi make spores (like seeds) that are resistant to drying out and to heat. If they get into the manufacturing process they may cause:

(a) a health hazard — they may be pathogenic

(b) financial loss if a whole batch of product is contaminated.

The usual precautions taken to prevent this from happening is for all equipment (fermenters, pipework, etc.) to be frequently steam-cleaned. The high temperature of the steam can kill the spores.

Bacteria and Nutrient Cycles

C2 *[Describe the part played by bacteria in the process of decay and recycling of carbon and nitrogen.]*

The Carbon Cycle

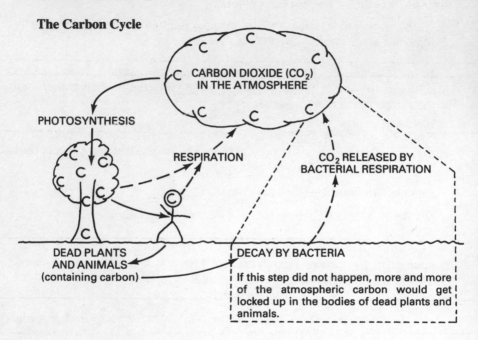

The Nitrogen Cycle

The following diagram is reproduced from Topic 1 (b). Here the emphasis is on the role of bacteria in the soil. Additional notes are provided below the diagram, relating to the processes numbered 1 – 4.

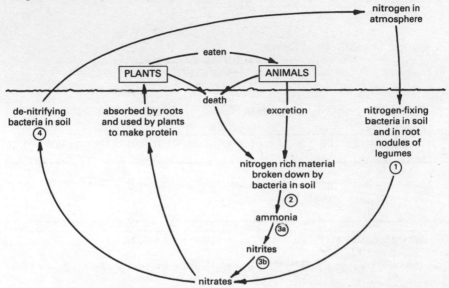

1. *Nitrogen fixing bacteria.* Found in soil and **root nodules** of legumes, i.e. peas, beans, clover, etc. They covert atmospheric nitrogen into *nitrates* which plants need to make protein.

2. *Decay bacteria in soil.* They break down dead plants and animals and animal excretions into *ammonia*.

3. *Nitrifying bacteria.* There are two types:

   (a) *Nitrite bacteria* which convert ammonium compounds into *nitrites*.

   (b) *Nitrate bacteria* which convert nitrites into *nitrates* for use by plants.

4. *Denitrifying bacteria.* They break down some of the useful nitrogen compounds in the soil and turn them back into atmospheric nitrogen.

Decay by Micro-organisms

C3 *[Explain how micro-organisms break down material to provide energy.]*

All living organisms need energy to survive. Micro-organisms such as bacteria and fungi use living or dead plant and animal material as an energy source.

Aerobic Breakdown of Sewage

C4 *[Explain why complete breakdown of sewage is only possible in aerobic conditions.]*

Anaerobic respiration (without oxygen) is much less efficient than aerobic respiration (with oxygen). Waste products of anaerobic respiration still contain a lot of energy. In other words the breakdown of the food is not complete.

Breakdown of sewage by anaerobic bacteria will always leave some sewage material untreated.

Aerobic bacteria however, will complete the breakdown, leaving only carbon dioxide and water.

$$\text{SEWAGE} \xrightarrow[\text{bacteria}]{\text{anaerobic}} \text{PARTIALLY DIGESTED SEWAGE (unsafe)}$$

$$\text{SEWAGE + OXYGEN} \xrightarrow[\text{bacteria}]{\text{aerobic}} \text{CARBON DIOXIDE + WATER (safe)}$$

C5 *[Explain why a range of micro-organisms is needed to break down the range of materials in sewage.]*

Sewage consists of many different types of waste material (carbohydrates, proteins, fats and minerals).

Each type of micro-organism tends to digest just one type.

Many different types of micro-organism are therefore needed to complete the treatment.

Advantages of Upgrading Waste

C6 *[Explain the advantages of upgrading waste in terms of increasing its available energy or protein levels.]*

Micro-organisms can take **low grade waste** with little energy or nutrient value and convert it to **high grade material** with a higher energy content or nutrient value.

Example 1

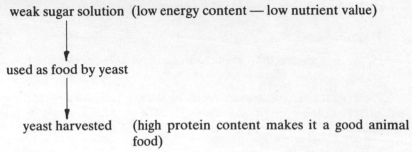

weak sugar solution (low energy content — low nutrient value)

used as food by yeast

yeast harvested   (high protein content makes it a good animal food)

Example 2

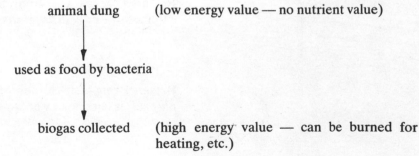

animal dung   (low energy value — no nutrient value)

used as food by bacteria

biogas collected   (high energy value — can be burned for heating, etc.)

149

SUB-TOPIC (c) — Reprogramming Microbes

Genetic Engineering

G1 *[State that the normal control of bacterial activity depends on the information stored in its chromosomes.]*

Scientists have discovered ways of changing bacteria so that they produce substances needed by humans. (See G4 page 151.) This is done by altering the **genes** on the chromosomes which control the activity of the bacteria. This technique is called *genetic engineering*.

Transferring Genes

G2 *[State that pieces of chromosome can be transferred from a different organism and so allow bacteria to make new substances.]*

Pieces of human chromosome can be transferred into a bacterial cell. The bacterium then produces the substance, e.g. insulin, made by the human genes.

1.

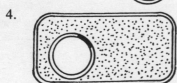

Required genes cut from human chromosome by *restriction enzymes*.

2.

Bacterial ring-like 'chromosome' (a *plasmid*) is cut open by enzymes.

3.

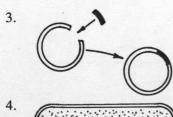

The piece of human chromosome is inserted into the bacterial plasmid.

4.

The plasmid is put back into a bacterial cell.

150

5.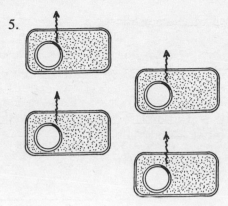

When the bacterium divides, each new cell contains the human genes and makes the desired substance which is released and can be collected.

$\Rightarrow$ C1/153 + C2/153 + C3/153

Products of Genetic Engineering

G3 *[Give some examples of the products of genetic engineering and their applications, e.g. insulin.]*

	Product	Application
1.	Insulin	For human diabetics, to control blood sugar.
2.	Growth hormone	To encourage growth in abnormally small children
3.	Washing powder enzymes	To digest biological stains at low temperatures.
4.	New antibiotics	Drugs designed to fight particular diseases.
5.	New strains of yeast	For more efficient brewing.
6.	"Built-in" pesticides	Genes inserted into plant cells so that the plant produces its own insect-killing chemicals.

$\Rightarrow$ C4/154

"Biological" Detergents

G4 *[State that "biological" detergents contain enzymes produced by bacteria.]*

"Biological" detergents contain enzymes produced by genetically engineered bacteria. These washing powders are good at removing stains such as grass, egg, blood, etc., which contain biological material.

$\Rightarrow$ C5/154 + C6/154

151

Antibiotics

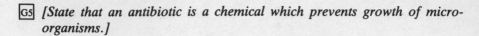 *[State that an antibiotic is a chemical which prevents growth of micro-organisms.]*

An antibiotic is a chemical which prevents growth of micro-organisms. The term **antibiotic** is normally used to describe a drug which kills or prevents the growth of **bacteria** inside the human body.

$$\Rightarrow C7/155 + C8/155 + C9/156$$

CREDIT LEVEL

Manipulating Chromosomes

C1 *[Explain genetic engineering in terms of manipulation of chromosomal material.]*

Genetic engineering can alter an organism's chromosomes by:

1. Adding new genes (often from a different organism).
2. Removing undesirable genes, e.g. those that may cause a disease.
3. Increase the number of copies of a desirable gene already present in an organism.

C2 *[State that as a result of genetic engineering, bacteria may produce increased quantities of products and speed up processes.]*

If several copies of a desirable gene are made and put into a bacterial cell, even greater quantities of the desired substance will be produced. Sometimes a bacterium's own genes may be copied to speed up a process carried out by the bacterium. For example, some bacteria can break down oil spills. If several copies of the gene involved are inserted, the bacterium will be able to clean up an oil spill much faster.

Genetic Engineering compared with Selective Breeding

C3 *[Explain how genetic engineering can be better than selective breeding for the production of new organisms for a particular function.]*

(N.B. For an explanation of selective breeding see Sub-Topic 6(c) page 131.)

If a new organism is needed to carry out a particular function, genetic engineering has the following advantages over selective breeding:

1. Genetic engineering is much faster. The new organism can be produced in just one or two generations. Selective breeding may take many generations.

2. Genetic engineering can give the new organism desirable characteristics that would never be developed by selective breeding, e.g. by incorporating genes from a different organism.

Note:
Genetic engineers must be **extremely** cautious when producing new strains of organism, particularly bacteria, as they may prove to have unpredictable and damaging effects if they are ever released into the environment.

The Demand for Insulin

C4 *[Explain the ever increasing need for insulin produced by biotechnology.]*

The hormone insulin is produced by the pancreas and controls the level of blood sugar. A diabetic is a person whose pancreas does not produce enough insulin. The number of diabetics is constantly rising due to people living longer and the human population growing.

Diabetics previously relied on animal insulin which was in limited supply and could cause side-effects. Human insulin can now be produced by genetically engineered bacteria.

"Biological" Detergents again

C5 *[Describe the advantages of using the low-temperature enzyme reactions of "biological" detergents.]*

C6 *[Explain the action of "biological" detergents in terms of digestion by enzymes.]*

"Biological" detergents, as well as being good at removing "biological" stains, have two other advantages over non-biological detergents. By working at low temperatures, they
1. save energy — less money spent on heating water;
2. do less damage to delicate fabrics that might be harmed in a hot wash.

The enzymes in biological detergents work by 'digesting' the biological material in the stain, making it easier to wash out. These detergents should be used at low temperatures, otherwise the enzymes may be destroyed.

Antibiotics again

C7 *[Explain why a range of antibiotics is needed in the treatment of bacterial diseases.]*

There are many different bacterial diseases which can infect different parts of the human body.

Examples:

'Ear-ache' — infection of the ear
Meningitis — infection of part of the brain
Sore throat — infection of back of the throat
Pneumonia — infection of the lungs.

A particular antibiotic may work well against one type of bacteria but not against another, which is said to be **resistant** to the antibiotic. Therefore a range of antibiotics is needed to fight bacterial diseases.

Immobilizing Enzymes

C8 *[Describe the advantages of immobilization techniques.]*

Enzymes are used in many manufacturing processes to convert raw materials into a product. Even with genetic engineering, enzymes may still be expensive to produce. To increase profit, the enzymes should be used many times if possible.

If the enzymes are just mixed with the substrate, it is difficult (and costly) to separate them from the end product and many enzymes will be lost.

Immobilization of the enzymes overcomes this problem.

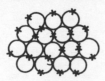

One way of immobilizing enzymes is to attach them to glass beads so that they can be **easily recovered** and **separated** from the end product.

155

Continuous-flow Processing by Immobilized Enzymes

C9 *[Explain continuous-flow processing by immobilized enzymes and the advantages this has over batch processing.]*

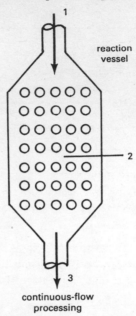

reaction vessel

continuous-flow processing

1. Substrate (raw material) is poured into the top of the reaction vessel in a steady stream.

2. Substrate trickles over enzymes held immobilized in the reaction vessel. The enzymes act on the substrate to produce the **product** which constantly trickles out at the bottom of the vessel (3).

Advantages over batch processing

1. Can be run for long periods without having to stop for cleaning, i.e. less time lost during which no product is being made.

2. Product does not have to be separated from substrate or enzymes as may be necessary in batch processing.

156

INDEX

159

Printed by Bell and Bain Ltd., Glasgow